# Spa
# RECIPES

### From The Spa
### at PALM-AIRE

1/92

Charlene,

Enjoy the
book in good
health. Keep in
touch. You have the
best sister anyone
can have. Just remember
you are lucky.
Love ya
Xavier

# Spa

# RECIPES

From *The Spa*

at PALM-AIRE

Tim Patton, M.P.H., M.A., R.D.
and Karen Manno

A MIDDLE ATLANTIC PRESS BOOK

A MIDDLE ATLANTIC PRESS BOOK

First Middle Atlantic Press printing, May 1989

ISBN: 0-912608-72-2

The Middle Atlantic Press, Inc.
848 Church Street
Wilmington, Delaware 19899

Distributed By:
National Book Network, Inc.
4720 A Boston Way
Lanham, Maryland 20706

# Introduction

The guests at The Spa at Palm-Aire are testimony to the fact that low fat, low sugar, low cholesterol, low salt meals are not only nutritious but also delicious. In response to numerous requests, we have compiled this cookbook in the hopes that it will help you begin a lifelong pattern of healthful eating.

The weight control success of the Palm-Aire Program is due largely to the application of the following philosophy: That is, eat small meals spaced throughout the day; eat a variety of food at each meal; minimize fats and sugars; include small amounts of lean protein; and center the meal around the carbohydrate, i.e. salads, vegetables, grains, and fruits. Of course, exercise is also an important part of the success of any weight control program.

Whether you are overweight and need to trim a few pounds, are at your ideal weight and want to maintain it, or wish to promote better health and prevent or treat many diet related illnesses such as heart disease, diabetes, or cancer, this book will help you prepare meals to assist you in achieving your intended benefits. The nutritional guidelines used for these recipes coincide with those established by the American Cancer Society, the American Diabetes Association, The American Heart Association and the Dietary Guidelines for Healthy Americans.

We wish you the best in your endeavors to eat well.

*With healthy regards,*

Tim Patton, M.P.H., M.A., R.D.
Nutritionist/Dietician

Karen Manno
Registered Diet Technician

# For Delicious and Nutritious Cooking We Suggest You Follow These Guidelines:

---

All products should be fresh, when possible.

All canned and frozen vegetable products are to be low in sodium.

All ingredients listed in capital letters are recipes that can be found in this cookbook.

All canned and frozen fruits are to be in their own natural juices, no sugar added.

All yogurt should be non-fat.

All cottage cheese should be 1% low fat.

All milk should be skim.

All low sodium broths should be chilled and skimmed of fat.

All spices and herbs can be used freely, except salt.

Arrowroot is a low calorie substitute for cornstarch. Mix with water before adding to ingredients.

Use low calorie or low fat ingredients when possible.

All cooking temperatures are based on Farenheit degrees.

# Table of Contents

# NUTRITION

Nutrition is the most important need of the human body, and eating is how we obtain the nutrition we need. Eating well in the *real* world involves the four important criteria:

- Adequately meeting our nutritional needs
- Fitting into the life we lead
- Liking the foods we eat
- Obtaining the results we want

Of all the nutritional needs, the most important need is for energy. Energy is required so we can think, move, and just stay alive. Because energy is so necessary, the body has an elaborate mechanism by which it can convert the energy from our foods into stored energy and conserve this energy for later use. This ability to store and conserve energy is so vital that we have been passing this trait down through the generations to the point where we now have a population of very efficient energy storers and conservers, i.e., fat people! An incredible portion of what now plagues us as disease and cause of death is a result of this phenomenon.

There are three categories of energy-containing nutrients: carbohydrates, proteins, and fats. They each provide energy in a different way, but a major difference is in the amount of energy they provide. Carbohydrates and proteins provide 4 calories per gram, whereas fat has 9 calories per gram. For example, the difference in calories between a pound of fat and a pound of sugar is as follows:

A pound of fat would have 4000 calories
A pound of sugar (carbohydrate) would have 1800 calories

As an energy source, fats are 2¼ times more concentrated.

Not only is the amount of calories important, but so is how our bodies use the energy. Carbohydrates from foods provide the body with an immediately utilizable source of energy called blood sugar. Of primary importance, blood sugar is the fuel we use for brain function. That is what makes this type of energy the most important need of our body. Without it (a condition known as *low blood sugar*, or *hypoglycemia*) the brain is deprived of fuel and responds by not working properly. The symptoms of low blood sugar are: being light-headed or dizzy, tired, and weak (think of 3:30 in the afternoon). To overcome this stress, the body has to make blood sugar (from stress hormones), so shaking, irritability, and nervousness may occur. If blood sugar deprivation continues, fainting, then coma, can occur—and, finally, death. And though permanent, death is not an acceptable means of weight control!

Not only is blood sugar from dietary carbohydrates needed by the brain, but it is the fuel we use to just stay alive. Our metabolism, the energy we expend without moving a muscle or thinking a thought, accounts for about ⅔ of all the energy output of a sedentary person each day. If there is not enough fuel to run the metabolism, it slows down, since this is how most calories are used each day. If metabolism is slower, food energy is less likely to be burned and, therefore, more likely to be stored as fat!

The third place blood sugar is used is in our working muscles. Some of the activities we perform—short bursts of muscle usage—require only blood sugar as a fuel. Most of what we do each day—dressing, eating, lifting, short walks, standing—are examples of blood-sugar-consuming activities, as are exercises like tennis, golf, weight training, push-ups, etc. Even when we are doing activities that will burn fat (aerobic exercises like walking long distance) we still need some sugar to help burn the fat.

So if carbohydrates are important because they provide blood sugar for brain function, metabolism, and muscles, why have they received such bad press? There is one place blood sugar will go if we consume more carbohydrates than can be burned—and that is to fat! Once blood sugar is turned into fat, it will never become available as blood sugar again. This means that if we consume a carbohydrate (simple sugars like sugar, honey, candy, soda, etc.) then blood sugar rises very quickly, and to avoid the blood sugar from going very high (diabetes) it is converted in a very short period of time to fat. As an example, a soft drink might immediately elevate the blood sugar and only be available for 15–30 minutes as this type of fuel before it is converted to fat. On the other hand, if a carbohydrate that is more complex for the body to break down to blood sugar (complex carbohydrates or starches) is consumed, then it will become blood sugar much slower. Therefore, it will cause less elevation and be available much longer to be used as energy. Though more likely to be used for energy, if over-eaten at one time even complex carbohydrates will produce more blood sugar than is needed, and the excess will be converted to, and stored as, fat!

Complex carbohydrates are needed in small to moderate amounts throughout the day.

Dietary proteins are absolutely essential because they are the only substrates that can be used to make body proteins like muscle, skin, enzymes, red blood cells, hair, hormones, etc. But because body proteins are so critical to life, our body will do everything possible to protect these proteins. This means that only a very small amount of dietary protein is actually needed each day.

For the average female and male, only 44 to 56 grams respectively are needed each day. This would be *no more than* 6–8 ozs. of animal protein per day, and since we also get some protein from complex carbohydrate foods, we do not need even this much. If more protein is consumed than is needed, the excess will be stored as fat. Once it becomes fat, it will never again be available to become body protein (i.e. fat will not turn into muscle).

Protein is also able to be converted to blood sugar. But if dietary protein goes to fat in excess, when blood sugar is needed (during a time when food has not been consumed) body protein is the only substrate available for this. The body is then actually burning itself as a fuel, and though an appropriate means of managing the crisis of supplying fuel to the brain (burning ourselves is better than dying), it is not something the body will do limitlessly. To conserve blood sugar and ultimately save very important body proteins, a slow-down process will occur (metabolic hypernotion). The more the body is deprived of energy, the greater the decrease of metabolism will be. With a slower metabolism, the energy from food will less likely be used, especially when normal eating is resumed, and therefore is more likely to be stored as fat. This effect is why so often, when a "diet" is used to lose weight, it results in weight loss as muscle, but weight gain as fat when the "diet" is stopped.

Not only will metabolism slow down with a major deficiency of energy, but so may physical activity (for instance, one feels tired or listless). Then it becomes less likely that one feels like taking long walks. As physical activity is decreased, the ability to burn fat is also decreased, because it is muscle tissue that is the only part of the body that efficiently uses this type of fuel.

The third type of energy-yielding nutrient is dietary fat. The purpose of fat is to provide concentrated energy for long-term storage. At one time when more energy was needed for physical activity, fat was necessary to provide enough calories. Unfortunately, in the last century the amount of fuel needed for physical work is only about one-third of what it was. Therefore, much less fat is needed to meet these energy requirements. Also important at one time was the need to have stored reserves of energy that could be conserved over time when the availability of food was limited (in winter, for example). At present, in our society, this need is no longer important. We have a continual supply of food year round. There is no longer a seasonal trend for fruits, vegetables, chocolate chip cookies, etc. This means much less fat is required as a stored reserve of fuel.

The problem with dietary fat is that nearly all (97%) of it will go from our food to our reserves (thighs, hips, abdomen, etc.) before it can be used as energy. The problem with all this fat going to reserves is that the only part of the body that will use stored fat for energy is muscle. In general, muscles will only burn fat when they are worked continually for an extended period of time. This is called aerobic exercise and examples are: walking, swimming, biking, etc.

Therefore, you *must* exercise to lose weight as body fat. Fat is the only kind of weight that is important to lose from both a health and a cosmetic perspective and your muscles are the only part of your body that will use fat as a fuel. So it follows: in order to lose appreciable amounts of fat, you are going to have to move your muscles!

In addition to using energy (calories) during physical activity, exercise affects your body in many ways that will put you at an increased weight-loss advantage. First, exercise will increase your metabolic rate for several hours after you have completed the activity as your "revved up" body returns to normal. This will also help counter the "diet"-related decreases in metabolism. Second, as you exercise, your body will be able to maintain or even increase your lean body mass. This is valuable because muscle is biologically active and will use calories even at rest. Third, exercise will make changes in your muscle cells that will allow them to use fat as a fuel more efficiently. You can actually change your physiology so that your body will choose to use fat as a fuel more frequently than it has in the past. Fourth, exercise will help you bring your appetite under control. Exercise causes an increased need for fuel in the blood, which often manifests itself as a feeling of satiety and a decrease in appetite.

By eating nutritious foods (complex carbohydrates) and by exercising aerobically, we obtain the results of being thinner and healthier. The difficult part is trying to fit eating well into our lives. There are five general rules, which can be used in every situation to help you.

The first rule in eating in the real world is to *plan* your meals.

We eat too much out of habit, and not enough thought goes into deciding what we are going to eat. In planning your meals, one of the most important principles is to eat more of your food during the active part of your day. For most of us that means eating larger amounts at breakfast and lunch, and less in the evening. It is not so much the number of calories consumed, but what time of day they are consumed.

The second rule is to eat a variety of foods at each meal. Your body requires many nutrients each day, and these can only be obtained from eating lots of different types of food. In addition, eating a wide variety of foods at each meal will keep us from feeling deprived.

Rule number three is that you have to have carbohydrate foods at each meal. Carbohydrates are the energy source that gives you energy to keep your metabolism running. When planning a meal, think first about the carbohydrates that you want and center your meal around these.

The fourth rule is to minimize fats when planning a meal. Fat is the most concentrated form of energy, and dietary fat must be stored as body fat before it can be utilized. In other words, fats are fattening, so limit the amount of fat in your meal. Also, sugar, when in quantity, will be stored quickly as body fat. So minimize fats all the time and sugars at any one time.

Protein should be the last food added to the planning process. Most people eat 3–4 times the amount of protein that they need every day. Excess protein is simply stored as fat, and once it has been converted to fat it is no longer available to the body as protein. In addition, protein, as derived from animals, is very high in fat, so it's easy to blow rule number four if protein is the center of the meal. Therefore, the fifth meal-planning rule is to add proteins last, choose the leanest, and use less.

The recipes in this book are an example of the philosophy of eating well. They meet the nutritional needs of the body. They are low in fat, low in sugar, low in cholesterol, and low in sodium.

The recipes presented in this book are nutritious and easy to prepare. Enjoyed by the clientele at Palm-Aire, they are low in calories and healthy for you!

# MEAL PLANNING

I.   PLAN YOUR MEALS through the day.

    A. Think about what you're going to eat at your meals.
    B. Eat more of your food at meals during the active part of your day and less food at inactive times.

II.  Eat a VARIETY OF FOODS at each meal.

    A. This provides the body with the nutrients it needs to stay healthy.
    B. A variety of foods at each meal helps prevent feeling deprived while trying to control your food intake.
    C. Include fresh fruits and vegetables; whole grains and grain products like breads, cereals, pastas, rice, etc.; low-fat dairy; and lean meats or meat alternatives.

III. Have a CARBOHYDRATE AT EACH MEAL.

    A. Center meals around the carbohydrate foods (fruits, vegetables, grains/cereals/breads).
    B. They supply the body, especially the brain, with utilizable energy. This allows you to feel good and energetic.
    C. Carbohydrate foods provide bulk (fiber) and a lot of water, therefore, they help fill you up with a minimum of calories.
    D. Plan carbohydrates in small amounts, to be eaten frequently through the day.

IV. Minimize your dietary FAT all the time and SUGAR at any one time.

    A. Fats are the most concentrated energy nutrient.
    B. Fats go to body fat before they can be used for energy.
    C. Fats are fattening.
    D. Excessive sugar turns to fat.

V. Don't worry about PROTEIN foods in the planning process.

    A. Most people eat far in excess (3–4 times) what they need, and the excess is stored as *fat*.
    B. Protein foods from animal derivatives contain *fat*.
    C. When using protein foods, have just a small amount at a time or in a day. Think of them as condiments.
    D. Add proteins to your meal LAST, LEAN, and LITTLE.

# NUTRITIONAL RECOMMENDATIONS

TO ASSURE AN ADEQUATE DIET, EAT A VARIETY OF FOODS, INCLUDING:

—Fruits
—Vegetables
—Whole grains, breads, cereals
—Low-fat dairy products
—Lean meat, poultry, fish, legumes

## TO LOSE WEIGHT:

—Exercise more
—Consume fewer fatty foods, sweets, and alcohol
—Improve eating habits

## TO AVOID FAT, SATURATED FAT, AND CHOLESTEROL:

—Choose lean meat, poultry, fish, and legumes
—Limit intake of above
—Avoid use of eggs and organ meats
—Avoid butter, cream, margarines, shortening, and foods made
  from these
—Limit intake of vegetable oils
—Use only 1% fat (or less) dairy products
—Trim excess fat or skin from meat and poultry
—Broil, bake, or boil, rather than fry
—Read labels for type and amount of fat in processed foods

## TO EAT MORE COMPLEX CARBOHYDRATES:

—Substitute starches for fats and sugars
—Use whole grain products, breads, and cereals
—Replace meat with beans and peas
—Include fruits and vegetables at each meal

## TO AVOID EXCESSIVE SUGARS:

—Use less of all sugars, including table sugar, honey, and
  syrup
—Avoid food containing sugars such as candy, soft drinks,
  cakes, cookies, ice cream, and other desserts
—Select fresh fruits or fruits canned without sugar
—Read labels for sugar content
—The frequency of sugar use is important as well as the amount
—Eat sweets less often

# VITAMIN/MINERAL CHART

| VITAMIN | SOURCES | FUNCTIONS |
| --- | --- | --- |
| A | Fortified milk, margarine, butter, eggs, liver, green leafy and yellow-orange vegetables and fruits. | Required for growth in children, promotes resistance to bacteria, good vision, healthy skin and hair. Prevents hardening and drying of the skin. |
| D | Fortified milk, cod liver oil, tuna, salmon, cheese, and egg yolk. | Helps form strong healthy teeth and bones. Necessary for calcium absorption. |
| E | Wheat germ and whole grains, vegetable oils, green leafy vegetables. | Prevents destruction of essential fatty acids and vitamin A. Helps form red blood cells, muscles, and other tissues. |
| K | Adults make this vitamin in their intestines. Also found in green leafy vegetables, cereals, and dairy products. | Essential for blood coagulation. |
| C | Broccoli, potatoes, citrus fruits and juices, vitamin-C fortified juices, and dark-green vegetables. | Forms collagen. Promotes use of calcium in teeth and bones. |
| THIAMINE | Pork, beef, liver, enriched food products, whole grains, peas, lima beans. | Part of the chemical reaction that releases energy from cabohydrates. |
| RIBOFLAVIN | Enriched and whole-grain foods, green leafy vegetables, lean meat, milk. | Assists in releasing energy for carbohydrates. Necessary for healthy skin and maintaining cell membranes. |

xviii

| | | |
|---|---|---|
| NIACIN | Enriched and whole-grain foods, legumes, meat, liver, eggs, and peanuts. | Works in conjunction with thiamine and riboflavin to release necessary energy from carbohydrates, and aids in fatty acid synthesis. |
| $B_6$ | Whole-grain food products, corn, green leafy vegetables, bananas, meat, potatoes, and nuts. | Needed for healthy teeth and gums, red blood cells, and the nervous system. Required for the absorption and metabolism of amino acids. |
| $B_{12}$ | Found only in foods of animal origin like lean meats, liver, milk, salt water fish, eggs, and cheese. | Helps form red blood cells. Aids in normal nerve function and growth. |
| BIOTIN | Made from bacteria in the intestinal tract. Also found in dark-green vegetables, egg yolks, organ meats, legumes, and nuts. | Necessary for metabolism of carbohydrates, protein, and fat. |
| PANTOTHENIC ACID | Found in almost all plant and vegetable foods. | Required in the chemical reactions that metabolize carbohydrates, protein, and fat. |

| MINERAL | SOURCES | FUNCTIONS |
|---|---|---|
| IRON | Red meats, oysters, clams, green leafy vegetables, dried fruits, enriched and whole-grain food products. | A major mineral, which helps carry oxygen to cells; also part of enzymes, protein synthesis, absorption of carbohydrates, and red blood cell formation. |
| CALCIUM | Milk and milk products, dark-green leafy vegetables, and fish with bones. | One of two major minerals found in bones and teeth. Necessary for muscle contraction and part of reaction that causes blood clotting. |
| PHOSPHORUS | Meat, fish, poultry, legumes, milk, and cheese. | Found with calcium as the largest part of bones and teeth. |

| MAGNESIUM | Raw, green leafy vegetables, whole grains, milk, and nuts. | Part of many enzyme systems. Maintains function of muscles, nerves, and body fluids. |
|---|---|---|
| ZINC | Meat, seafood, milk, legumes, and eggs. | Essential for most biochemical process and metabolism in the body. |
| COPPER | Nuts, liver, corn oil, margarine, legumes, shellfish, grapes, cereal. | Needed for normal metabolism of iron, and for functioning of several enzymes needed for respiration. |
| IODINE | Fresh seafood, iodized salt, water. | Needed for normal metabolism. |
| FLUORIDE | Fluoridated water, plant and animal tissue. | Strengthens teeth and bones, prevents cavities. |

# VEGETABLES

Vegetables can add variety and a generous supply of important nutrients to your meals. They are particularly high in vitamins A and C. The dark, leafy vegetables are naturally low in calories and high in fiber, which helps to fill you up, not out.

A serving is one measuring cup of the following foods and contains 10 grams of carbohydrate, 4 grams of protein, and no fat, for a total of 50 calories per serving. Foods should be measured after cooking.

Artichokes
Asparagus
Bean Sprouts
Beans (Green, Wax)

Beets
Broccoli
Brussels Sprouts
Cabbage

Carrots

Cauliflower

Eggplant

Greens (Mustard, Turnip,
   Collard)

Italian Beans

Kohlembi

Mushrooms

Okra

Onions

Pea Pods

Peppers (Green)

Rutabaga

Sauerkraut

Spinach

Summer Squash

Zucchini

If eaten raw, one measuring cup of the following vegetables contains 5 grams of carbohydrate, 2 grams of protein, and no fat for a total of 25 calories.

Bean Sprouts

Broccoli

Cabbage

Carrots

Cauliflower

Celery

Cucumber

Lettuce

Mushrooms

Peppers (Green)

Radishes

Spinach

Tomatoes

# FRUITS

Fruits naturally contain sugar, which makes them sweet and a welcome addition to almost any meal. In addition to sugar, fruits also contain a large amount of fluid, which helps to decrease their calories. Fruits are high in many vitamins, especially A and C, and in some minerals, and contain fiber, which helps move food through the digestive tract.

Each serving of the following fruits contains 15 grams of carbohydrate, and no protein or fat, for a total of 60 calories per serving, if fresh, frozen, or canned without added sugar.

| 1 Small | 1 Cup | ½ Cup |
|---|---|---|
| Apple | Blackberries | Applesauce |
| Frozen Juice Bar | Blueberries | Cherries |
| Mango | Raspberries | Fruit Cocktail |
| Pear | Strawberries | Grapes |
| | Watermelon | Mandarin Orange |
| | | Pineapple |
| | | |
| | | Apple Juice |
| | | Cranberry Juice |
| | | Grape Juice |
| | | Grapefruit Juice |
| | | Orange Juice |
| | | Pineapple Juice |
| | | Prune Juice |

| 2 Small | Other |
|---|---|
| Apricots | ½ Banana |
| Dates | ½ Cantaloupe |
| Figs | ½ Casaba Melon |
| Nectarines | ½ Grapefruit |
| Peaches | ¼ Honeydew Melon |
| Plums | 2 Tbsp. Raisins |
| Tangerines | |

# STARCHES

Starch is an important source of energy. It is naturally low in fat and high in many vitamins, such as thiamin ($B_1$), riboflavin ($B_2$), and niacin ($B_3$), as well as iron. If the type of starch eaten is whole grain, it is also high in fiber.

One measuring cup of the following foods contains 30 grams of carbohydrate, 6 grams of protein, and no fat, for a total of 150 calories per serving. Foods should be measured after cooking.

## Cereals

Cooked:
  Cream of Wheat
  Cream of Rice
  Farina
  Oatmeal
Dry, Unsweetened:
  Bran Flakes
  Corn Flakes
  Shredded Wheat (2 Biscuits)
  Special K
  Total

## Grains/Pasta

Barley
Corn (12" Corn-on-the-Cob)
Grits
Rice (White or Brown)
Macaroni
Noodles
Rigatoni
Spaghetti

## Legumes

Black Beans
Blackeyed Peas
Kidney Beans
Lentils
Navy Beans
Split Peas
Soy Beans

## Breads

Bagel (1)
Bread Sticks (4–4 inches long)
English Muffin (1)
Frankfurter or Hamburger Bun (1)
Melba Toast (10)
Pita (1–6 inch)
Plain Roll (large)
Rye or Pumpernickle Bread (2)
Tortilla (2)
White, French, or Italian Bread (2)
Whole Wheat Bread (2)

## Crackers/Snacks

Animal Crackers (16)
Graham Crackers (6)
Matzoh (2 oz.)
Oyster Crackers (48)
Popcorn (6 cups)
Pretzels (2 oz.)
Saltine-Type Crackers (12)
Whole Wheat-Type Crackers (6)

## Starchy Vegetables

Lima Beans
Peas
Potato (1 large)
Winter Squash
Yams

# DAIRY

Dairy foods provide protein, calcium, and riboflavin ($B_2$). Dairy products made from whole milk contain high amounts of fat, therefore low-fat dairy products are recommended.

The following foods contain 12 grams of carbohydrate, 8 grams of protein, and no fat, for a total of 80 calories per serving.

| 1 Cup | ½ Cup |
|---|---|
| Skim Milk | Evaporated Skim Milk |
| 1% Low Fat Milk | Low Calorie Pudding |
| 1% Low Fat Buttermilk | Low Fat Cottage Cheese |
| | Low Fat Farmer's Cheese |
| | Plain, Coffee, Lemon-Lime, or |
| | Vanilla Low Fat Yogurt |

# FATS

Fats do not contribute any significant nutrients to meals, but do provide a large number of calories per serving. For this reason, fats should not be used often.

One serving of the following foods contains 5 grams of fat and no protein or carbohydrate, for a total of 45 calories per serving.

| 1 Teaspoon | 1 Tablespoon |
| --- | --- |
| Butter | Coffee Whitener, Powder |
| Corn Oil | Cream Cheese |
| Cottonseed Oil | Margarine, Diet |
| Margarine | Mayonnaise, Reduced Calorie |
| Olive Oil | Salad Dressing |
| Mayonnaise | |
| Safflower Oil | |

# MEATS

Meats and meat substitutes, like fish and chicken, contribute high quality protein, niacin ($B_3$), and iron to meals. They also contain fat and, therefore, need to be limited. The leanest cuts, like those listed below, should be used.

A serving is three ounces (cooked weight) of the following foods and contains 21 grams of protein, 9 grams of fat, and no carbohydrate, for a total of 165 calories per serving.

| Beef | Pork | Poultry (No Skin) |
| --- | --- | --- |
| Bottom Round | Canadian Bacon | Chicken |
| Flank Steak | Lean Ham | Turkey |
| Pot Roast | Tenderloin | Cornish Hen |
| Rump | | |
| Top Round | | |

| Lamb | Veal (Avoid Cutlets) |
|---|---|
| Leg | Chops |
| | Roast |

## Fish/Seafood

| | |
|---|---|
| Bass | Lobster |
| Clams | Oysters |
| Cod | Perch |
| Flounder | Sardines (Water Packed) |
| Grouper | Scallops |
| Halibut | Shrimp |
| Herring (Uncreamed) | Snapper |
| | Sole |
| | Tuna (Water Packed) |

## Other

95% Fat Free Luncheon Meats

# BREAKFAST & BREADS

## Jarlsberg Egg White Omelette

2 egg whites
½ ounce Jarlsberg cheese
  shredded

Vegetable coating spray (Pam)

Beat egg whites and pour into preheated pan sprayed with Pam and cook over medium heat until bottom is firm. Add cheese, fold omelette in half, allow time for cheese to melt completely, remove from heat and serve. 75 calories.

# Spanish Omelette

½ cup chopped green pepper
¼ cup chopped onion
1 tablespoon garlic juice
1 canned California green chili
   chopped
½ small tomato, squeezed of
   juice and chopped

2 teaspoons chopped pimento
6 egg whites
Pinch of saffron
½ cup low fat cottage cheese
CHILI SALSA (optional)

In skillet, sauté green pepper and onion in garlic juice and 2 tablespoons of water. Add chopped chili, tomato and pimento and boil off remaining liquid. Combine egg whites and saffron and beat to soft peaks. Fold cheese into egg whites, followed by the contents of the skillet. Return to skillet and fry until eggs are set, turning to avoid scorching. Pour off any water rendered during cooking. (Serve topped with Chili Salsa if desired.) Serves 2. 1 serving = 100 calories.

# French Toast with Apples

2 egg whites
2 slices bread
¼ cup non-fat milk
½ teaspoon vanilla

½ teaspoon cinnamon
½ cup cooked unsweetened
   apples

Beat egg whites until frothy, add milk and seasoning. Dip bread into mixture. Place on rack under heated broiler and broil each side about three minutes, or brown in a non-stick pan. Serve hot with apples on top. 200 calories.

# Breakfast Bagels

Use those bagels in the freezer for a quick, popular breakfast.

*6 bagels*
*1 cup low fat cottage cheese*
*2 medium-to-large tomatoes*

*1 medium sweet red onion,*
  *sliced*

Split each bagel into 2 circular half-bagels. Lay bagel halves, cut face up, on broiler pan. Cover each bagel with thin layer cottage cheese. Slice each tomato into six slices. Lay one tomato slice and one onion on each bagel. Broil until edge of bagel toasts. Serves 6. ½ bagel = 100 calories.

# Bagel Melt

*½ bagel, sliced in half*
*Tomato slices*

*1 ounce Jarlsberg cheese*

Place cheese on bagel slices and put in broiler for one minute or until cheese melts. Garnish with tomato slices. 200 calories.

# Quiche

4 slices whole wheat bread
  (preferably stale)
1 cup low fat cottage cheese
1 3½ ounce can evaporated skim
  milk

¾ cup egg whites
1 tablespoon minced parsley
2 small onions, minced
Add pepper to taste

Line 10-inch pie plate with bread. Spread with cottage cheese and onions. Combine remaining ingredients in blender. Cover, blend until smooth. Pour over onion layer. Bake in preheated 425 degree oven 35 to 40 minutes. Cut into squares to serve. Makes 6 servings. 1 serving = 110 calories.

# Strawberry Crêpes

2 prepared CRÊPES
½ cup cut strawberries

MOCK SOUR CREAM (2
  ounces non-fat yogurt
  seasoned to taste with lemon
  juice)

Put strawberries on each crêpe, roll the crêpe and cover with the yogurt and lemon mix. 1 serving. 200 calories.

# Crêpe Recipe

½ cup whole wheat flour
¼ teaspoon salt
5 egg whites

1 cup skim or low fat buttermilk
1 tablespoon safflower oil

Combine dry ingredients. Beat egg whites until fluffy. Add milk and oil to egg whites. Add liquids to flour mix and stir until smooth. Batter will be thin. Drop on a non-stick preheated griddle, using about 1½ ounces per crêpe. Brown lightly on both sides. Crêpes will roll more easily if they are not over-cooked. Recipe makes ten crêpes. Those not served immediately can be frozen. Stack with wax paper between crêpes to prevent sticking, wrap securely and store in the freezer to be used as needed. 1 crêpe = 40 calories.

# Cheese Blintz with Pineapple

2 prepared CRÊPES
2 ounces low fat cottage cheese

2 ounces canned, crushed,
unsweetened pineapple

Spread prepared crêpes with 1 ounce of low fat cottage cheese, top with 1 ounce cooked pineapple and roll crêpe. If necessary, use low-calorie sweetener to taste. 200 calories.

# Buckwheat Pancakes with Blueberries

*1½ cups whole wheat flour*
*1 teaspoon baking powder*
*2 egg whites, slightly beaten*

*1 cup skim milk*
*2½ cups cooked blueberries*

Combine milk and egg whites. Sift flour and baking powder together and stir into milk mixture until moistened. Drop batter onto heated non-stick pan. Cook until bubbles appear, turn and cook other side. Serve warm with ¼ cup cooked blueberries on each pancake. Makes 10 pancakes, 5 servings. 1 serving = 2 pancakes. 200 calories.

# Velvety Pancakes

*1 cup whole wheat flour*
*1 teaspoon baking powder*

*2 egg whites*
*1½ cups evaporated skim milk*

Combine baking powder and flour. Beat egg whites to soft peaks, add milk and beat again. Combine wet and dry mixtures, stir lightly. Teflon-fry pancakes on both sides. Top with a FRUIT SAUCE*. Makes 12 to 14 pancakes. 1 serving = 2 pancakes. 100 calories.

*For FRUIT SAUCE recipe see BLUEBERRY SAUCE in Sauce section.

# White Bread

*1 envelope active dry yeast*          *6-7 cups flour*
*2¼ cups water*

Preheat oven to 400 degrees. Sprinkle yeast on ¼ cup lukewarm (105 degrees) water and let soften a few minutes. Combine 2 cups warm (120 degrees) water and 2 cups of the flour, add softened yeast, and beat with electric mixer for 3 minutes. Add remaining flour a cup at a time until dough can be handled. Turn out onto heavily floured board and knead until smooth and elastic (about 5 minutes). Let rise in a warm place, in a smooth, floured bowl until double in bulk (about 30 minutes). Shape into two loaves. Place in Teflon baking pans and let rise again until double (1 or more hours). Bake 1 hour at 400 degrees. Makes 2 loaves. 1 loaf = 1,200 calories. ¹⁄₁₆ loaf = 75 calories.

# Dinner Rolls

*1 envelope active dry yeast*          *1 egg white*
*1 cup skim milk*                      *4½ cups unbleached white flour*

Sprinkle yeast onto surface of ¼ cup warm (120 degrees) water. Scald milk, cool to lukewarm (105 degrees), and pour into large bowl. Add dissolved yeast, egg white and 2 cups flour. Beat until smooth, then mix in rest of flour. Turn out onto floured board, and knead until smooth and elastic (about 5 minutes). Place dough in lightly greased bowl, then turn dough in bowl, bringing bottom side up. Cover with towel wrung out in hot water, place in warm place (about 80 degrees), and let rise until double in bulk (1 to 1½ hours). When doubled, punch down and place on floured board. Roll or pat dough until it is 1 inch thick. Cut with small drinking glass into biscuit shapes, place on Teflon pan, and let rise until doubled (about 45 minutes). Preheat oven to 400 degrees. Bake 20 to 25 minutes at 400 degrees. Makes 20 rolls. 1 roll = 95 calories.

# Oatmeal Bread

3 cups rolled oats
1 teaspoon salt
2 tablespoons vegetable oil
¼ cup molasses
1 package yeast

1½ to 2 cups whole wheat flour
½ cup skim milk
3½ cups all-purpose flour
3 cups water
½ cup wheat germ

Preheat oven to 400 degrees. Put the yeast, oats, salt, wheat germ, whole wheat and 1 cup white flour in large bowl. Heat water, milk, oil and molasses mixture until lukewarm. Pour into dry mixture. Mix. Stir in enough flour to make stiff dough. Turn out on floured board and knead in rest of flour, about 10 minutes. Put dough in greased bowl, turn to grease top. Let rise until doubled in bulk. Punch dough down. Form into two loaves. Place seam-side down in two greased loaf pans. Let rise until doubled in bulk. Bake 45 minutes in 400 degree oven. One serving = ¹⁄₁₆ loaf. 100 calories.

# Banana Bread

2 cups whole wheat flour
2 teaspoons baking powder
½ teaspoon baking soda
½ teaspoon ground nutmeg

4 egg whites
½ cup vegetable oil
2 tablespoons sugar
3 over-ripe bananas (mashed)

Preheat oven to 350 degrees. Combine the flour, baking powder, baking soda, and nutmeg in a mixing bowl. Stir to blend. Put the eggs, oil, sugar and bananas in blender. Puree until smooth. Pour the banana mixture into the flour. Mix well. Pour into a Pam-sprayed 9-by-5-inch loaf pan. Bake in a 350 degree oven for 40 to 50 minutes. Cool on a wire rack. Let stand 10 minutes before removing from pan. Cool thoroughly before serving. One serving = ¹⁄₁₅ of loaf. 150 calories.

# Pumpkin-Bran Muffins

1 cup whole wheat flour
½ cup bran
1 tablespoon sugar
2 teaspoons baking powder
½ teaspoon baking soda
½ teaspoon ground cinnamon
2 tablespoons vegetable oil
½ cup cooked or canned
  pumpkin
2 egg whites
¾ cup orange juice
⅓ cup dark or golden raisins
1 tablespoon wheat germ

Preheat oven to 400 degrees. Combine all the ingredients, except the wheat germ, in a mixing bowl. Stir to blend. Spoon into lightly oiled muffin tins. Sprinkle on the wheat germ. Bake in a 400 degree oven for 10 to 15 minutes. 1 serving = one muffin. 150 calories.

# Bran Muffins

½ cup whole wheat flour
½ cup unprocessed bran flakes
2 tablespoons baking powder
2 egg whites
1 tablespoon safflower oil
¼ cup black strap molasses
¼ cup honey
¼ cup finely diced apple
½ cup boiling water
1 teaspoon cinnamon
½ teaspoon nutmeg
¾ cup skim buttermilk
Vegetable coating spray (Pam)

Preheat oven to 325 degrees. Combine flour, bran and baking powder. In a separate bowl, mix apple, cinnamon, nutmeg and boiling water and place in refrigerator to cool. Combine beaten egg, oil, molasses, honey, buttermilk and apple mixture with dry ingredients and gently fold together. Portion into lightly sprayed muffin tin. Bake at 325 degrees for 35 minutes. Makes 12 muffins. One muffin = 75 calories. Muffins may be frozen.

# Biscuits

1½ cups all-purpose flour
½ cup whole wheat flour
1 tablespoon baking powder
½ teaspoon salt

3 tablespoons diet margarine
A scant ¾ cup skim milk
Bran, wheat germ, or seeds for
    topping

Preheat oven to 400 degrees. Mix flour, baking powder and salt. Cut in the margarine until it makes a coarse dough. Add milk slowly. Dough will be sticky. Mix dough only until all liquid is absorbed and dough holds together. Sprinkle small amount of flour into bowl. Flour hands. Knead dough in bowl about one or two minutes. Shape into balls, place on ungreased cookie sheet and flatten. Bake in 400 degree oven 10 to 12 minutes. 1 serving = one biscuit. 100 calories.

# Orange Muffins

2 cups all-purpose flour
6 packets Sweet 'N Low
1 tablespoon baking powder
½ teaspoon salt
2 egg whites

1 cup skim milk
2 tablespoons diet margarine,
    melted
2 teaspoons finely grated orange
    rind

Preheat oven to 425 degrees. Spray muffin tin with non-stick coating. Sift dry ingredients into bowl. In separate bowl, combine egg whites with milk, margarine and orange rind. Beat with fork or whisk to mix thoroughly. Make a well in center of dry ingredients. Pour in liquid ingredients. Stir quickly until dry ingredients are just moistened and mixture is slightly lumpy. Divide batter into muffin tin cups, each two-thirds full. Bake 15 to 20 minutes, or until golden brown and toothpick inserted in center comes out clean. Loosen edges of muffins. Let stand one or two minutes. 1 serving = one muffin. 90 calories.

# Chocolate Chip Banana Bran Muffins

1 cup shredded bran cereal (such as Kellogs All Bran or Fiber One)
½ cup plus 2 tablespoons skim milk, at room temperature
1½ cups sifted all purpose flour
¼ cup granulated sugar
¼ cup miniature semi-sweet chocolate chips

1 tablespoon baking powder
¼ teaspoon salt
1 cup mashed ripe bananas (approx. 2 large bananas)
2 large egg whites at room temperature
Vegetable coating spray (Pam)
¼ cup vegetable oil

Position a rack in the center of the oven and preheat to 400 degrees. Lightly spray Pam on 12–2¾ × 1¼ (3 ounce) muffin cups. In a medium bowl combine the bran and milk. Let stand 3-4 minutes until soft. In a large bowl stir together the flour, sugar, chocolate chips, baking powder, and salt. In another bowl stir together the bananas, egg whites, oil and softened bran mixture until blended. Make a well in the center of the dry ingredients. Add the liquid ingredients and stir with a wooden spoon just to combine. Spoon the batter into the prepared muffin cups making each cup ¾ full. Bake 20-25 minutes or until the muffins are golden brown and a cake tester or toothpick inserted into the center of one muffin comes out clean. Cool the muffins in the pan on a wire rack for 5 minutes. Remove the muffins from the cups and finish cooling on the rack. Serve warm or cool completely. You may store muffins in an airtight container at room temperature for up to 12 days. 12 muffins. 175 calories each.

# Potato Pancakes

4 baked potatoes
1 cup low fat cottage cheese
Chives and black pepper to
    taste

¼ cup skim milk

Remove potato filling. Discard skins. Add cottage cheese, chives, black pepper & milk to potato mixture. Mix all together and shape into 8 pancakes. 2 pancakes per serving. Serves 4. 175 calories. Serve with unsweetened applesauce.

# APPETIZERS & SOUPS

## Potato Skins

1 medium sized baking potato
2 teaspoons of freshly grated
  parmesan cheese

Hungarian paprika

Wrap potato in aluminum foil and bake in 425 degree oven for about one hour. Remove potato and slice in half. With a spoon scoop out as much potato as possible without tearing the outer skin. Place one teaspoon of parmesan cheese over each half with a sprinkle of ground paprika. Place under broiler for one minute and serve. Makes 2 potato skins. 2 servings = 70 calories.

## Quick Tortilla Chips

6 corn tortillas
Onion powder to taste

Garlic powder to taste

Preheat oven to 400 degrees. Cut each tortilla into eight triangles. Place triangles on cake rack and bake 6 minutes. Turn chips over, sprinkle with garlic, onion or both. Bake 3 minutes more. Makes 48 chips (a nice bowlful). Use with any dip. Goes especially well with CHILI SALSA. 1 Chip = 8 calories.

# Chili Salsa

3 fresh jalepeño chilies
3 fresh yellow chilies
2 fresh California green chilies
2 medium tomatoes, chopped (4
  tomatillos)
½ teaspoon garlic flakes

½ medium onion, chopped
1 stalk celery, chopped fine
½ teaspoon coriander seeds (or
  ¼ cup finely chopped
  cilantro)

Seed the chilies, saving a teaspoon or so of the seeds to make the salsa hot. Chop the chilies and combine all ingredients except the seeds in a saucepan. Add ½ cup water. Add seeds, ⅛ teaspoon at a time, tasting for spiciness at each addition. Stop at desired spiciness. Cover and simmer 3 hours. Use on tacos, in beans, on refried beans, in burritos or in any other dish to give a spicy Mexican flavor. Store in refrigerator or freezer. Makes 2 cups. 1 cup = 40 calories.

# Leek Soup

6 cups chicken broth (low
  sodium)
1 cup fresh leeks in one-inch
  slices
1 clove garlic, crushed

½ teaspoon black pepper
½ teaspoon arrowroot
1 teaspoon Veg-It seasoning (no
  salt seasoning)

Combine all ingredients, bring to a boil and simmer for 20 minutes. Serve hot. Serves 6. 1 serving = 40 calories.

# Liver Paté

4 ounces raw chicken liver
1 teaspoon chopped garlic
1 teaspoon chopped onions
1 teaspoon chopped celery
1 teaspoon parsley
Dash of thyme

Dash of black pepper
¼ teaspoon dry mustard
1 tablespoon skimmed chicken
   broth
Lettuce and tomato slices

Braise chicken livers in broth with celery and onion in non-stick skillet for 8 to 12 minutes. Drain off juice and puree with the rest of the ingredients in blender. Refrigerate. Serve on lettuce leaf with tomato slice garnish. Serving size 1 ounce chicken liver per person = 40 calories.

# Stuffed Mushrooms

12 large fresh mushrooms
¼ medium onion
⅛ cup Miller's Bran
   (unprocessed bran)
½ celery stalk

¼ cup skim milk
2 ounces crab meat (fresh, frozen
   or canned)
2 teaspoons Veg-It (no salt
   seasoning)

Place all ingredients except mushrooms in food processor or blender. Blend well. Stuff mushrooms with the mixture and bake 10 to 15 minutes at 350 degrees, or until top is browned. Serve immediately. Serves 6. Two mushrooms per serving = 40 calories.

# L.A. Bean Dip

1 cup cooked pinto beans, drained
2 canned California green chilies, chopped

2 tablespoons plain non-fat yogurt
½ teaspoon onion powder
Pinch of cayenne pepper

Combine ingredients and mash in small saucepan. Cook to desired consistency. Makes 1¼ cups. 1 ounce = 30 calories.

# Pineapple-Cheese Dip

½ cup low fat cottage cheese
¼ cup skim milk
1 tablespoon lemon juice
Pinch of celery seeds

2 tablespoons unsweetened pineapple juice
Dash of pepper

Combine all ingredients in blender. Blend at high speed until very smooth. Serve chilled with crackers or tortilla chips. Makes ¾ cup at 75 calories.

# Salmon Dip

1 7¾ ounce can of salmon
2 tablespoons minced green onion (scallion)
¼ cup plain non-fat yogurt
¼ cup diet mayonnaise
½ teaspoon ground ginger

2 tablespoons sesame seeds, toasted
Raw vegetables: zucchini, celery, carrots, pea pods, cherry tomatoes

Drain and flake the salmon. Combine all the ingredients, except the raw vegetables, in a bowl. Cover and refrigerate at least one hour. Serve with the vegetables. 1 serving = 1 tablespoon. 15 calories per serving.

# Potato Hors D'oeuvres

18 small red skinned potatoes
½ pound fresh mushrooms
1 tablespoon dried dill
1 tablespoon dried parsley flakes

½ cup unsweetened apple juice
1 teaspoon lemon juice
3 tablespoons grated parmesan
  cheese

Wash the potatoes and steam them until they are fork-tender. Cut off a thin slice on the bottom of each potato to allow it to sit without rolling. Cut off a thin slice on top of each potato and scoop out the inside "meat." Reserve the inside. Poach the mushrooms in a saucepan with the dill, parsley flakes, apple juice and lemon juice for 5 minutes. Pour off the liquid. Put the mushrooms and potato flesh in a food processor or blender. Chop until fine. Stuff the potato skins with the mushroom filling. Sprinkle with cheese. Refrigerate until ready to serve. When ready to serve, heat in a 350 degree oven for 15 to 20 minutes. Serve warm. 1 serving = 1 potato. 50 calories.

# Cottage-Egg Salad Spread

12 hard cooked egg whites,
  chopped
1 8 ounce carton low fat cottage
  cheese
1 teaspoon chopped olives

½ teaspoon dry mustard
¼ teaspoon pepper
½ to 1 teaspoon dried whole
  dillweed

Combine all ingredients; mix well. Cover and chill. Serve on whole wheat toast. 1 ounce = 20 calories.

# Consommé au Sherry

1 quart CHICKEN STOCK
4 ounces sherry
1 clove garlic, crushed

2 tablespoons dried or fresh
chopped parsley

Combine all ingredients in 2 quart saucepan. Bring to a boil and simmer 15 to 20 minutes. Serves 6. 1 serving = 40 calories.

# Chicken Stock

1 whole chicken, cut up (skin
removed excluding giblets)
½ bay leaf
¼ teaspoon peppercorns
2 stalks celery, whole
1 bundle fresh herbs (parsley,
chervil and thyme) tied with
a string

1 small onion, quartered
1 green pepper, seeded and
quartered

Cut meat from bones and put all ingredients (bones included) into a stew pot with 6 cups of cold water. Gradually bring to a boil and simmer until meat is tender (2 to 3 hours). Strain, and put aside the chicken meat for use in other recipes. Season with pepper to taste, cool, skim fat and store in refrigerator or freezer until needed. Makes 1 quart. 20 calories per ½ cup serving.

# Beef Stock

6 pounds beef bones
1 gallon water
1 onion, cut up
2 carrots, cut up

6 mushrooms, cut up
Other vegetable tops and greens,
    as available
¼ teaspoon pepper

In large pot, bring all ingredients to a boil. Cover and simmer 6 to 10 hours. Strain, chill and skim fat. Makes about 3 quarts. 1 cup = 30 calories.

# French Onion Soup

4 medium onions, chopped        4 cups BEEF STOCK

Place ½ cup of onions and 2 tablespoons of stock in a saucepan. Heat slowly until onions start to brown, stirring only occasionally. Stir and continue to brown and even burn onions. Add remaining onions and ¼ cup of stock. Stir, cover and simmer 5 minutes. Uncover and stir and cook until liquid has evaporated and onions are dry and brown. Add remaining stock and simmer 20 minutes. Makes 5 cups. 1 cup = 30 calories.

# Zucchini Consommé

4 ounces CHICKEN STOCK        Mrs. Dash (no salt seasoning)
⅓ cup shredded zucchini

Bring stock to a boil and simmer 15 to 25 minutes. Reheat with zucchini; season to taste with Mrs. Dash. Serves 1. 45 calories.

# Tomato Soup

*1 cup tomato juice (low sodium)*    *Mrs. Dash*
*½ cup CHICKEN STOCK*    *Black pepper*

Combine juice and stock, bring to a boil and simmer 20 minutes, seasoning to taste. Serves 2. 1 serving = 40 calories.

# Gazpacho

*3 6 ounce cans low sodium V-8*    *⅓ cup chopped green pepper*
  *juice*    *⅓ cup chopped onion*
*⅓ cup chopped cucumber*

Combine ingredients in blender. Chill and serve. Serves 4. 1 serving = 40 calories.

# Neptune's Chowder

2 pounds fillets of firm fleshed
    fish (e.g., halibut, red
    snapper or sea bass)
3 large potatoes
1 medium onion, chopped
1 medium leek, chopped
1 stalk celery, chopped
1 clove garlic, minced finely
1 large carrot, diced

1 20 ounce can tomatoes, chopped
1 cup tomato sauce (low sodium)
2 tablespoons parsley flakes
2 bay leaves
¾ teaspoon thyme
Dash of pepper
¾ cup sherry wine
1 medium lemon
3 tablespoons arrowroot

Cut fish into 1½ inch cubes and set aside. Boil potatoes until tender but not soft, then peel and dice. Place onion, leek, celery and garlic in a large soup pot. Add ½ cup water, cover and cook over medium heat until vegetables are tender and slightly yellow (about 15 minutes). Add carrot, tomatoes, tomato sauce, spices, and simmer, covered 30 minutes. Add wine, juice of the lemon, the cut-up fish and the diced potatoes, and simmer 20 minutes more. Mix arrowroot with ⅓ cup cold water, stir into the simmering pot. Cook and stir until chowder thickens. Cook a few minutes more and serve. Serves 8. 1 cup = 160 calories.

# Chicken Noodle Soup

3 quarts water
1 small chicken, cut up (skin
  removed)
1½ cups celery, diced
3 large carrots, chopped
1 large onion, sliced

1 teaspoon garlic powder
1 teaspoon oregano
1 teaspoon pepper
1 bay leaf
2 cups cooked shell macaroni

Prepare chicken, add to water with seasonings and cook on medium heat for 2 hours. Remove chicken and cut up meat, set aside. Chill and skim broth. Add vegetables and cook until tender, approximately 1 hour. Add 1 cup of cut up chicken and cooked noodles, bring to a boil. Serves 4-6. 1 serving = 100 calories.

# Bean-Pea Soup

1 cup dried pinto beans
1 cup dried navy beans
1 pound package of dried split
  peas
3 stalks celery, diced

2 small onions, chopped
3 carrots, diced
8 whole peppercorns
¼ teaspoon dry mustard

Bring 3½ quarts water to boil in large kettle, add beans and peas, and boil 2 minutes. Turn heat off, cover kettle, and let sit 1 hour. Then add the rest of the ingredients and simmer covered until the beans are soft and the soup is thick (about 2 hours). Puree half the contents of the soup in a blender, return puree to kettle, stir well, and serve. Makes 3 quarts. ½ cup = 40 calories.

# Greek Lentil Soup

1 cup lentils, washed and
  drained
2 quarts CHICKEN STOCK, or
  water
1 medium onion, chopped
3 tablespoons tomato paste (low
  sodium)

1 stalk celery, chopped
1 bay leaf
¼ teaspoon oregano
2 tablespoons wine vinegar

Without disturbing the boil, slowly pour lentils into vigorously boiling stock. Add all other ingredients except vinegar, reduce heat and simmer, stirring occasionally, until lentils are very soft (about 1½ hours). Add vinegar. Puree half of the soup in the blender, return pureed portion to pot, mix, heat and serve. Makes 2 quarts. 1 cup = 130 calories.

# Split Pea Soup

1 pound split peas, 2-2½ cups
1 cup chopped celery
1 quart BEEF STOCK
½ cup tomato juice
2 tablespoons arrowroot

1 cup chopped onions
¼ teaspoon marjoram
½ teaspoon pepper
1 quart water
¼ teaspoon thyme

Soak split peas overnight in stock, water and tomato juice. Drain peas, reserving liquid. Add enough water to liquid to make 2 quarts and return peas to liquid. Bring to boil, reduce heat and simmer 2 hours. Add vegetables and spices and simmer 30 minutes or longer. Blend with arrowroot and serve. Makes 6 cups. 1 cup = 110 calories.

# Potato Soup

1 cup sautéed onions (sauté in 2
   tablespoons water)
2 cups diced potatoes

1 cup chopped celery
1 cup evaporated skim milk

Add ingredients, except milk, to 4 cups of boiling water. Cover and boil gently 30 minutes or until tender. Add milk. Let simmer 10 minutes. Mash if desired. Serves 8. 1 cup = 65 calories.

# Crock Pot Stew

1 large can low sodium V-8
   juice

Fresh vegetables (whatever you
   have on hand will work:
   cauliflower, broccoli, fresh
   green beans, potatoes,
   summer squash, onions, fresh
   peas, among others)

Wash and cut vegetables into bite-sized pieces. Put all vegetables into a slow cooker. Add the can of V-8 juice and fill the pot to the top with water. Spices may be added, but little is needed. Put slow cooker on high for 2 hours, then turn to low and let cook until vegetables are tender (around 6-8 hours). This is a great soup to put on before going to work in the morning, as it will be ready when you get home. 1 cup = 60 calories.

# Cream of Turkey Soup

1 small meaty turkey carcass
1 quart water
1 onion, sliced
2 tablespoons sherry
½ pound fresh mushrooms,
  finely chopped
Vegetable coating spray (Pam)

13 ounce can evaporated skim
  milk
1 tablespoon flour
Parsley flakes and pepper to
  taste (optional)
Pinch nutmeg

Combine turkey carcass, water, onion, sherry, and nutmeg in kettle. Simmer covered 2 hours. Strain broth; cool to room temperature. Refrigerate until fat hardens; remove and discard fat. Separate meat from bones; reserve meat. Discard bones and skin. Brown mushrooms in Pam in large nonstick skillet. Add reserved turkey meat and broth. Heat to boiling. Mix together milk and flour, stir into skillet. Cook and stir over moderate heat until hot and bubbling. Sprinkle with parsley and pepper. Makes 6 servings. 120 calories per serving.

# Minestrone Soup

10 ounce package frozen mixed
  vegetables
2 cups low sodium tomato juice
1½ cups fat-skimmed chicken or
  beef broth, low sodium
1 cup minced celery
½ cup chopped onion
1 clove garlic, minced

1 teaspoon dried oregano
Pinch thyme or poultry
  seasoning and pepper to
  taste (optional)
2 cups diced cooked poultry or
  leftover lean roast beef,
  trimmed of fat

Combine all ingredients except meat in large saucepan. Heat to boiling; reduce heat. Simmer covered 10 minutes. Stir in meat. Simmer covered 10 more minutes or until heated through. Makes 4 servings. 150 calories per serving.

# Spicy Corn Soup

2 teaspoons diet margarine
½ cup chopped onion
2 cups cooked corn kernels
2 cups canned or homemade low
    sodium CHICKEN BROTH
1 cup diced green bell pepper
1 cup evaporated skim milk

2 tablespoons drained, canned,
    chopped green chilies
½ teaspoon freshly ground
    pepper
2 tablespoons fresh cilantro
Leaves to garnish (optional)

In medium saucepan over medium heat, heat margarine until bubbly. Add onion; sauté until soft. Scrape into blender; add corn and 1 cup of the broth; blend until almost smooth. Pour back into saucepan; add the remaining 1 cup broth, the bell pepper and milk; bring to a boil. Reduce heat to low; simmer 10 minutes, stirring occasionally. Stir in chilies and ground pepper. Makes 4 servings. 180 calories.

# Beef Consommé Celestine

4 ounces BEEF STOCK
    skimmed of fat (low sodium
    package bouillon cubes or
    broth may be used)

4 to 5 eggless noodles (pasta)
Chopped parsley
Mrs. Dash

Heat beef stock with eggless noodles. Bring to boil and simmer 15-25 minutes. Add chopped parsley and Mrs. Dash to taste. Serves 1. 40 calories.

# Garbage Soup

¼ cup chopped onion
1 16 ounce can of low sodium
  chopped tomatoes
3-4 cups any frozen or leftover
  cooked vegetables: corn,
  green beans, spinach, broccoli,
  carrots, cauliflower, peas,
  cabbage and legumes

1 small clove garlic, minced
10 peppercorns or ½ teaspoon
  coarsely ground pepper
¼ teaspoon oregano
1 bay leaf
1 tablespoon parsley
6 cups water

Combine all ingredients and simmer for 20 minutes. Leftover meat or chicken, rice, pasta or potatoes may also be added. Serves 4-6. 1 serving = 40 calories.

# Lamb-Barley Soup

Meaty bone from roast leg of
  lamb
2 quarts water
¼ cup chopped fresh parsley and
  pepper to taste (optional)
2 cups sliced carrots
2 cups sliced onions

2 cups sliced celery
1 16 ounce can tomatoes, well
  broken up, undrained low
  sodium tomatoes
6 tablespoons medium pearl
  barley

Combine lamb bone, water, parsley and pepper in kettle. Simmer covered 1 hour. Strain broth; cool to room temperature. Refrigerate until fat hardens; remove and discard fat. Separate meat from bones; discard bones. Wrap and refrigerate meat. Stir vegetables and barley into broth. Simmer covered 1½ hours, or until barley is tender. Stir in reserved meat and heat through. 100 calories per serving. Makes 10 servings.

# Mushroom Clam Chowder

1 cup fresh mushroom stems
   and pieces
1 teaspoon safflower or
   sunflower oil
1 can (7 or 8 ounce) minced
   clams, undrained, low
   sodium
1 stalk celery, chopped
1 small onion, chopped

1½ cups cold water
1 tablespoon arrowroot and
   pepper to taste (optional)
Pinch cayenne pepper
2 tablespoons minced fresh
   parsley
4 ounces low sodium CHICKEN
   BROTH
1⅓ cups non-fat dry milk powder

Sauté mushrooms in oil in nonstick saucepan. Stir in chicken broth, clams, celery, and onion. Simmer covered 5 minutes. Mix together milk powder, water, arrowroot and peppers; stir into saucepan. Cook and stir over low heat just until soup bubbles and thickens. Sprinkle with parsley before serving. Makes 4 servings. 80 calories per serving.

# Cold Fruit Soup

1 cup non-fat yogurt
¾ cup puréed fruit (any fresh
   fruit is best)

Skim milk (consistency)
Equal (or sugar substitute to
   taste)

Mix yogurt and puréed fruit in blender; add skim milk for a soup like or soupy consistency and add equal for taste. Chill. 40 calories.

28

# Lentil Stew

¾ cup chopped onions
¾ cup chopped celery
6 cups water
¾ cup dried lentils, washed and
  sorted
2 16 ounce cans whole salt free
  tomatoes, undrained and
  chopped

¾ cup uncooked brown rice
2 cloves garlic minced
½ teaspoon dried basil
½ teaspoon dried oregano
¼ teaspoon black pepper

Saute onion and celery in diet margarine in a dutch oven until tender; add water and lentils. Bring mixture to a boil; cover, reduce heat, and simmer 20 minutes. Stir in next 6 ingredients. Cover and simmer 1 hour or until rice is done. Add carrots; cook an additional 5 minutes. Can substitute any type of pasta for rice. 1 cup = 50 calories.

# SALADS & DRESSINGS

## Hearts of Palm

2 hearts of palm spears,          1 teaspoon tarragon vinegar
  canned                          Basil and parsley

Thoroughly wash canned liquid from hearts of palm. Cut spears
down the middle. Place two spears on a lettuce leaf per serving, season with vinegar, basil and parsley. 40 calories.

## Artichoke Hearts Vinaigrette

2 artichoke hearts, halved        Diet Italian salad dressing

Marinate artichokes in diet dressing for two hours. Remove
from dressing, place on lettuce leaf with chopped parsley and
lemon wedge. 1 serving = 40 calories.

# Asparagus Spears

5 asparagus spears
Lemon wedge

Lettuce or other greens

Cook and chill asparagus (see vegetable cooking chart). Arrange with lemon wedge. 40 calories.

# Seafood Cocktail

1 ounce of poached seafood
  (may be crab, shrimp or
  lobster)

Lettuce or other greens
1 ounce COCKTAIL SAUCE
Lemon wedge

Place seafood on bed of greens and top with sauce. Serve with lemon wedge. 40 calories.

# Cole Slaw

1½ cups shredded white
  cabbage
½ cup shredded carrot

1 tablespoon celery seed
MUSTARD SAUCE to taste

Mix all ingredients well. For better taste, let stand for several hours in refrigerator. Serves 4. 1 serving = 4 ounces. 20 calories.

# Spinach and Mushroom Salad

*½ cup fresh spinach, washed
and deveined*

*4 large fresh mushrooms*

Pull spinach apart into bite size pieces and portion into bowls. Slice mushrooms and place over spinach. Chill well. Serve with 1 tablespoon diet dressing or lemon juice. Serves 2. 1 serving = 20 calories.

# Stringbean and Mushroom Salad

*½ cup mixed cut green beans
or mushrooms*

*MUSTARD SAUCE
Lettuce or other greens*

Place beans and mushrooms on bed of greens and top with 1 ounce of mustard sauce. 20 calories.

### MUSTARD SAUCE

*1 8 ounce jar diet whipped
dressing (Milani) or diet
mayonnaise*

*3 tablespoons dry mustard
¼ cup boiling water*

Mix dry mustard with boiling water until dissolved. Add to whipped dressing. Chill. Serving size = 2 ounces. 50 calories.

SPA RECIPES FROM THE SPA AT PALM-AIRE

# Beet and Onion Salad

¼ cup sliced cooked beets          1 ounce red wine vinegar
1 slice of onion

Combine ingredients, let stand for one hour, serve on lettuce leaf. 1 serving = 20 calories.

# Fresh Broccoli, Mushroom and Carrot Curl Salad

1 large fresh mushroom, cleaned     Lettuce leaf
1 carrot curl, 3 to 4 inches long   Pimento slice
1 broccoli floweret

Arrange vegetables on lettuce, garnish with pimento, serve with 1 tablespoon diet dressing. 1 serving = 20 calories.

# Shredded Carrot Salad

½ cup shredded carrots              Lettuce leaf
½ ounce (1 teaspoon) YOGURT-
   PINEAPPLE DRESSING

Serve carrots on lettuce leaf, topped with dressing. Makes 1 serving. 40 calories.

# Rainy Day Salad

1 large beet, cooked, cooled,
   diced
1 large potato, cooked, cooled,
   diced
1 stalk celery, diced

1 medium apple, diced
1 medium green pepper, diced
2 tablespoons BUTTERMILK
   SPRING DRESSING

Toss all ingredients lightly. Moisten with Buttermilk Spring Dressing and tint with some of remaining beet juice. Serves 6. 1 cup = 100 calories.

# Taco Salad for 12

1 pound extra lean ground
   beef crumbled, cooked, drained
   and cooled
1 15 ounce can of kidney beans,
   drained and rinsed under
   cold running water
1 head Romaine lettuce, chopped

2 tomatoes, chopped
1 bunch green onions, chopped
1 recipe of QUICK TORTILLA
   CHIPS
1 large head lettuce, chopped
3 cups low fat cottage cheese

Dressing: CHILI SALSA and low sodium tomato juice mixed to taste.

Combine all ingredients except tortilla chips and salsa. Before serving, crush and add tortilla chips. Top with dressing. Serves 12. 1 cup = 150 calories.

# Green Bean Aspic

1 12 ounce can of unsalted
  vegetable juice
1 tablespoon unflavored gelatin
1 teaspoon lemon juice
1 cup cooked and thoroughly
  drained frozen, French-cut
  green beans

½ cup cooking liquid from green
  beans (or water)

Pour ¼ cup vegetable juice into a flat bowl. Sprinkle gelatin evenly over surface, and let soften 5 minutes. Combine lemon juice and beans, toss thoroughly and set aside. Bring liquid from green beans to a boil, add to gelatin and stir to completely dissolve all beans and pour into aspic mold. Chill until set, unmold and serve. Serves 4. ⅓ mold = 50 calories.

# Mixed Green Salad

There are many ways to make a mixed green salad. Any greens and vegetables will do. This recipe is delicious and well liked. (Be sure to use dark-leaf lettuce in every salad.)

1 head iceberg lettuce
1 head romaine lettuce
2 large tomatoes, diced
1 small cucumber, peeled and
  diced

½ cup carrots, grated
2 tablespoons green onion,
  chopped
¼ cup mushrooms, sliced

Toss all ingredients and serve. Makes 5 large salads. 1 salad = approximately 2 cups. 50 calories.

# Antipasto Garbanzos

*2 tablespoons cider vinegar*  
*¼ cup water*  
*1 clove garlic, minced*

*¼ cup chopped onion*  
*1 cup cooked garbanzo beans*

Combine vinegar, water, garlic and onion to make a marinade for the garbanzo beans. Marinate beans for 3 hours or more, adding a bit of water to the marinade if necessary to cover the beans. Serve as an appetizer or as a salad topping. 1 ounce serving = 30 calories.

# Four Bean Salad

*1 cup cooked kidney beans*  
*1 cup cooked green beans*  
*1 cup cooked wax beans*  
*½ cup cooked garbanzo beans*  
*½ cup apple juice*

*½ cup chopped onion*  
*1 tablespoon chopped pimento*  
*1 teaspoon onion powder*  
*½ teaspoon pepper*  
*2 teaspoons vinegar*

Combine all ingredients and marinate in refrigerator several hours. Makes 1 quart. ½ cup serving = 90 calories.

# Holiday Salad

¾ cup fresh asparagus tips,
   steamed
¾ cup fresh green beans,
   steamed
¾ cup diced cucumbers
½ cup raw young peas

½ cup sliced radishes
2 artichoke hearts, cooked and
   sliced
2 egg whites, hard-cooked and
   sliced

Toss all ingredients lightly. Serves 6. 1 serving = 35 calories.

# Buttermilk Coleslaw

¾ cup skim buttermilk
1 tablespoon lemon juice
2 tablespoons regular dry
   non-fat milk

¾ teaspoon pepper
¾ teaspoon celery seed
3 cups shredded cabbage
½ cup shredded carrots

Combine all ingredients except cabbage and carrots, and mix
well to make creamy coleslaw dressing. Toss cabbage and carrots with dressing and let sit two hours before serving. Makes 1
quart. ½ cup = 20 calories.

# Potato Salad

4 cups peeled, diced and
  cooked potatoes
5 egg whites, hard-cooked, diced
1 cup chopped celery
¼ medium onion, chopped
3 tablespoons chopped green
  onion
3 tablespoons chopped green
  pepper

2 teaspoons cider vinegar
1 tablespoon parsley flakes
¼ to ½ teaspoon garlic powder
½ teaspoon pepper
1½ teaspoons Italian seasoning
1 cup plain non-fat yogurt
4 teaspoons prepared mustard
  (or to taste)

Combine all ingredients except yogurt and mustard. Combine
yogurt and mustard, and stir into other ingredients. Refrigerate
two or three hours before serving. Makes 6 cups. ½ cup = 70
calories.

# Dill Dressing

3 cups non-fat yogurt
1½ teaspoons pepper
1½ teaspoons garlic powder

Dash of Tabasco Sauce
Dash of Worcestershire Sauce
½ cup fresh chopped dill

Mix all ingredients well with wire whisk. 1 tablespoon = 10
calories.

# Pineapple-Cottage Cheese Salad

1 8 ounce can of pineapple
  tidbits juice packed,
  unsweetened
2 tablespoons juice from
  pineapple

4 cups low fat cottage cheese
¼ cup evaporated skim milk
½ head shredded lettuce

Combine half of the pineapple tidbits, 1 cup of the cottage cheese, the pineapple juice and the skim milk in the blender and chop and blend until very smooth. Add remainder of pineapple tidbits and cottage cheese and blend for a few seconds only. Serve over shredded lettuce. Serves 8. 1 serving = 100 calories.

# Fruit and Cottage Cheese Salad

6 leaves of lettuce
3 cups of low fat cottage cheese
6 strawberries
2 medium apples, quartered,
  cored and sliced thin

1 cup pineapple chunks
2 oranges, sectioned and seeded
3 bananas, sliced
1 bunch seedless grapes
3 cups melon balls

On individual salad plates, make a bed with a lettuce leaf, place a mound of cottage cheese in the center, arrange bite-size pieces of fruit around the mound, and top it with a strawberry. Makes 6 individual fruit salads. 1 cup serving = 115 calories.

# Garden Salad

1 cup mixed iceberg and
   romaine greens
¼ cup shredded carrot and
   summer squash

1 tomato wedge

Place lettuce in bottom of bowl, top with shredded vegetables and garnish with tomato wedge. Serve with one tablespoon of your choice of low calorie dressing. 20 calories (without dressing).

# Romaine Salad

1 cup chopped romaine lettuce
2 cherry tomatoes

1 tablespoon diet salad dressing

Place tomatoes on lettuce in salad bowl. Serve with dressing. 20 calories (without dressing).

# Bibb Lettuce Salad

½ cup bibb lettuce shredded
¼ cup sliced onion

¼ cup shredded carrot
2 cherry tomatoes

Combine in bowl. Serve with one tablespoon low calorie dressing. 20 calories (without dressing).

# Tomato and Onion Salad

3 tomato slices, ¼ inch thick
2 onion slices, about ⅛ inch
   thick

Lettuce or other greens

Place tomatoes on a bed of greens, top with onion slices. Chill well. Serve with one tablespoon low calorie dressing. 20 calories.

# Broccoli, Cauliflower and Carrot Salad

1 small sliced carrot
1 broccoli floweret

1 cauliflower floweret
1 leaf lettuce

On lettuce leaf arrange carrots, cauliflower and broccoli attractively. Garnish with a thin slice of pimento. Serve with one tablespoon low calorie salad dressing. Serves 1. 20 calories.

# Marinated Mushrooms

2 cups sliced mushrooms
½ cup tarragon vinegar

½ teaspoon black pepper

Combine mushrooms, pepper and vinegar in mixing bowl and chill 1½ hours. Portion ½ cup of marinated mushrooms over a lettuce leaf. Garnish with a slice of lemon. Makes 4 servings. ½ cup = 25 calories.

# Cold Pasta or Rice Salad

*Cooked pasta or rice (chill)*
*Steamed mixed vegetables (chill)*
*Low-cal (diet) Italian dressing,*
  *seasoning to taste*

*Pepper and/or Mrs. Dash*

Cool pasta or rice, add the cool vegetables and mix in the Italian dressing (lightly). Chill and serve. 1 cup = 100 calories.

# Snow Peas and Cucumber with Dill

*2 cups stringed snow peas*
*1 cup pared seeded cucumber*
  *strips*

*2 tablespoons snipped fresh dill*
*2 teaspoons lemon juice*
*Freshly ground pepper*

In medium bowl, combine first 3 ingredients. Season to taste with pepper; sprinkle with 2 teaspoons water. Cover and steam until vegetables are crisp-tender. Sprinkle with lemon juice and toss to mix. Makes 4 servings of about ½ cup each. 1 serving = 40 calories.

# Mixed Veggie Salad

1 pound broccoli flowerets
1 pound cauliflower flowerets
2 medium carrots, scraped and
  thinly sliced
1 medium size purple onion,
  thinly sliced
1 medium green pepper cut into
  one inch pieces

1 15 ounce can garbanzo beans,
  drained
1 cup sliced pitted black olives
1 8 ounce bottle low-cal Italian
  dressing

Combine everything, toss gently. Cover and chill one hour. ½ cup = 70 calories.

# Avocado Salad

½ head iceberg lettuce, torn
10 cherry tomatoes, halved
1 large avocado, peeled and
  chopped

3 pitted black olives, sliced
⅓ cup low calorie 1000 Island
  dressing
1 teaspoon chili powder

Mix all together. Serves 6. 1 serving = 130 calories.

# Sunshine Carrot Salad

2 cups grated carrots
1 11 ounce can mandarin
  oranges, drained
1 cup pineapple chunks, packed
  in own juices, drained
1 cup flaked coconut

½ cup raisins
½ cup chopped walnuts
1 8 ounce carton plain low fat
  yogurt
Lettuce leaves

Combine first 6 ingredients; stir well. Chill 2-3 hours. Stir in yogurt. Serve salad on lettuce leaves. Serves 6-8. 1 cup = 200 calories.

# Light Asparagus Vinaigrette

2 packages frozen asparagus
  spears
½ cup vinegar
½ cup water
½ pound fresh spinach leaves
2 tablespoons chopped fresh
  chives

2 tablespoons Dijon mustard
½ teaspoon dried whole tarragon
2 medium tomatoes, cut into
  wedges

Cook asparagus according to directions; drain, place in shallow container. Combine next 6 ingredients, mix well. Pour over asparagus. Chill 3 to 5 hours. Place asparagus on spinach leaves; pour dressing over salad. Garnish with tomatoes. 51 calories per serving. Serves 6.

# Marinated Cucumbers and Artichokes

2 medium cucumbers, peeled
  and thinly sliced
1 14 ounce can artichoke hearts
  drained and cut in halves
¼ cup vegetable oil
1 onion grated

½ teaspoon dry mustard
½ teaspoon garlic powder
½ teaspoon basil
⅛ teaspoon black pepper
⅛ cup vinegar

Put cucumbers and artichokes in medium bowl. Mix remaining ingredients, pour over mixture and toss lightly. Cover and refrigerate over night. Serves 4-6. 1 serving = 100 calories.

# Waldorf Salad

1 large banana, sliced
2 large apples, cored and diced
3 teaspoons lemon juice
2 tablespoons skim milk
2 tablespoons coarsely chopped
  walnuts

¼ cup dark or golden raisins
2 tablespoons diet mayonnaise
Lettuce leaves

Put the apples and banana in a medium-size bowl and add the lemon juice. Toss. Add the celery, walnuts and raisins. In a small bowl, beat the mayonnaise and milk until smooth; toss with the apple mixture. Serve on lettuce. ¼ of salad = 150 calories.

# Bleu Cheese-Buttermilk Dressing

8 ounces 1% low fat cottage
  cheese
2 ounces 1% low fat buttermilk

1 ounce ripe bleu cheese
1 teaspoon Mrs. Dash
1 teaspoon lemon juice

Blend all ingredients in a blender until creamy smooth. This dressing is also delicious as a dip and a topping for baked potatoes. 1 tablespoon = 25 calories.

# Cucumber Dressing

3 cups non-fat yogurt
1½ teaspoons pepper
1½ teaspoons garlic powder

Dash of Tabasco
1 whole cucumber

Grind cucumber in food processor. Combine with yogurt and spices and mix well. 1 tablespoon = 13 calories.

# Yogurt-Pineapple Dressing

4 ounces plain non-fat yogurt

2 ounces unsweetened pineapple
  juice

Blend well and chill before serving. 1 ounce serving = 16 calories.

# Spiced Vinegar Dressing

¼ cup wine or cider vinegar
2 tablespoons water
1 tablespoon lemon juice
1 tablespoon onion flakes
1 tablespoon parsley flakes

¼ teaspoon pepper
¼ teaspoon tarragon
¼ teaspoon oregano
¼ teaspoon paprika

Mix ingredients, chill and stir before serving. Goes great as a light dressing on tossed salads. Makes ½ cup. 1 tablespoon = 10 calories.

# Bleu Cheese Dressing

Over ripe Bleu Cheese
Skim milk or skim buttermilk

1 cup low fat cottage cheese

Scrape moldiest areas off bleu cheese to get 1 tablespoon of very concentrated bleu cheese. Stir into cottage cheese and thin to desired consistency with skim milk or skim buttermilk. Makes 1 cup of delicious bleu cheese dressing. 1 tablespoon = 20 calories.

# Garlic and Vinegar Dressing

2 cloves garlic, sliced
½ cup vinegar
¼ cup water
¼ teaspoon paprika

½ teaspoon ground thyme
2 tablespoons frozen apple juice
.  concentrate

Combine all ingredients and shake well before serving. Makes ¾ cup. 2 tablespoons = 10 calories.

# Creamy Salad Dressing

1½ cups low fat cottage cheese
½ teaspoon garlic powder

1 tablespoon lemon juice
Buttermilk

Combine ingredients in blender and blend until smooth. Buttermilk helps the flavor and may be used in thinning. Excellent on vegetables or tossed salads. Makes 1½ cups. 1 tablespoon = 10 calories.

# Perfection Salad Dressing

1½ cups unsweetened pineapple juice
1½ cups tomato juice (low
   sodium)
2 tablespoons fresh lemon juice
2 garlic buds, pressed

2 tablespoons chopped pimento
2 tablespoons chopped capers
¼ teaspoon freshly ground
   pepper
¼ teaspoon dry mustard

Combine all ingredients and mix thoroughly. Store tightly covered in refrigerator. Makes 3 cups. 1 tablespoon = 10 calories.

# Pimento Dressing

1 cup MOCK SOUR CREAM
  or low fat cottage cheese

2 tablespoons pimentos

Place ingredients in blender, chop, then liquify at high speed. A mild, sweet dressing. Makes 1 cup. 1 tablespoon = 11 calories.

# Tangy Salad Dressing

¾ cup tomato juice (low
  sodium)
2 tablespoons finely chopped
  onion

3 tablespoons lemon juice
¼ teaspoon pepper

Combine all ingredients, chill and stir before serving. Makes 1 cup. 1 tablespoon = 10 calories.

# Buttermilk Spring Dressing

1 cup skim buttermilk
1 teaspoon frozen apple juice
  concentrate
1 teaspoon lemon juice

1 teaspoon onion flakes
1 teaspoon dill weed
Pepper
Ground allspice

Mix all ingredients except pepper and allspice. Add pepper and ground allspice to taste. (Begin with about ⅛ teaspoon each and add more if necessary.) Chill. Makes 1 cup. 1 tablespoon = 11 calories.

# Creamy Cottage Cheese Dressing

*1 cup low fat cottage cheese*          *¼ cup skim milk*

Place cottage cheese in blender, slowly add skim milk and blend until creamy smooth. Add spices to taste. We suggest garlic or onion powder, pepper, dill, Mrs. Dash, or oregano. 1 tablespoon = 18 calories.

As a dressing for fruit, add 2-3 packages of Equal to the skim milk and cottage cheese and blend. At the end of blending add ½ teaspoon vanilla.

# Spicy Tomato Cocktail

*1 cucumber*
*6 cups canned (low sodium)*
  *tomato juice*
*3 green onions (scallions)*
  *chopped*

*2 tablespoons lemon juice*
*Dash of Tabasco Sauce*
*1 teaspoon Worcestershire Sauce*
*1 tablespoon prepared horseradish*

Peel and grate the cucumber. Add it to the tomato juice with the remaining ingredients. Cover and refrigerate 2 hours or overnight. Strain before serving. 1 serving = 1 cup. 40 calories.

# SAUCES

## Versatility Sauce

This delicious sauce can really "make" a dish. Use it on Green Bean Casserole or over any pasta. Goes well on meats and other dishes as well.

1 medium green pepper, chopped
   fine
1 medium onion, chopped fine
1 stalk celery, diced
1 clove garlic, minced

2 tablespoons whole wheat flour
1½ cups tomato juice*
½ teaspoon oregano flakes
½ teaspoon basil

Sauté green pepper, onion, celery and garlic in 2 tablespoons water, until tender (about 5 minutes). Sprinkle flour evenly over top, add tomato juice, oregano and basil and cook and stir over medium heat until sauce thickens. Makes 2 cups. *Use a 3-to-1 mixture of low sodium to regular tomato juice to add a little saltiness to the flavor in a controlled manner. 1 cup = 40 calories.

# Spaghetti Sauce

2 28 ounce cans of tomatoes
2 cups tomato sauce (low
   sodium)
1 large onion, chopped
½ cup dry burgundy wine

1 tablespoon grated parmesan
   cheese
1½ tablespoons oregano flakes
1 teaspoon basil
1 teaspoon garlic powder

Blend tomatoes in blender, place in a saucepan and cook and stir over high flame until cooked down to a thick consistency (about 45 minutes). Add remaining ingredients while tomatoes are cooking. Makes 2½ quarts. 1 cup = 56 calories.

# Spaghetti Sauce #6

This recipe, straight from the *Live Longer Now* Cookbook, is a favorite.

3 28 ounce cans of tomatoes,
   packed in puree
2 cups chopped fresh mushrooms
2 medium onions, chopped
1 medium green pepper, chopped
1 stalk celery, chopped

1 tablespoon garlic flakes
1 tablespoon parsley flakes
1 tablespoon oregano flakes
1 teaspoon thyme
1 teaspoon pepper
1 teaspoon basil

Chop tomatoes briefly in blender. Combine all ingredients in a large saucepan, add ¼ cup water, cover and simmer slowly 2 hours. Makes 3 quarts. 1 cup = 50 calories.

# Mushroom Sauce

Simple as can be, this sauce is terrific as a base for tuna and other casseroles.

½ cup sliced fresh mushrooms          2 tablespoons water
1 tablespoon garlic juice             2 cups WHITE SAUCE

Sauté mushrooms in garlic juice and water. Combine with white sauce and heat. Makes 2¼ cups. 1 cup = 100 calories.

# Chili Salsa

3 fresh jalepeño chilies              ½ medium onion, chopped
3 fresh yellow chilies                1 stalk celery, chopped fine
2 fresh California green chilies      ½ teaspoon coriander seeds (or
2 medium tomatoes, chopped (4            ¼ cup finely chopped
   tomatillos)                           cilantro)
½ teaspoon garlic flakes

Seed the chilies, saving a teaspoon or so of the seeds to make the salsa hot. Chop the chilies and combine all ingredients except the seeds in a saucepan. Add ½ cup water. Add seeds ⅛ teaspoon at a time, tasting for spiciness at each addition. Stop at desired spiciness. Cover and simmer 3 hours. Use on tacos, in beans, on refried beans, in burritos or in any other dish to give a spicy Mexican flavor. Store in refrigerator or freezer. Makes 2 cups. 1 cup = 40 calories.

# Compromise White Sauce

1 tablespoon diet margarine
1 cup skim milk

2 tablespoons flour
Dash of white pepper

Combine margarine and 1 tablespoon of the skim milk in a small saucepan. Heat and mix until margarine melts and is evenly mixed with milk. Remove from heat, add flour and mix. Begin cooking over low heat. Add small amounts of the remaining milk while cooking and stirring constantly. Use all milk. Cook slowly until thickening is nearly complete. Add pepper and cook until fully thickened. Makes 1 cup. 1 cup = 100 calories.

# Cranapple Relish

1 apple
1 naval orange, peeled
2 cups fresh or frozen
  cranberries

2 packets Equal sweetener
¼ teaspoon nutmeg or cinnamon
½ teaspoon ground coriander
  (optional)

Shred the apple in a food processor or with a hand grater. Quarter the orange and combine with the cranberries in a food processor or food grinder. Process until coarsely chopped. Blend the apple, cranberry mixture, coriander, nutmeg, cinnamon and sweetener together. Cover and refrigerate until ready to serve. Makes 6 servings. 1 serving = ½ cup. 40 calories.

# Curried Pea Sauce

1 10 ounce package of frozen
  peas
1 cup skim milk

2 tablespoons chopped pimento
1 tablespoon arrowroot
1 teaspoon curry powder

Place peas in a saucepan, add ½ cup water, cover and cook over medium heat until tender (5 to 8 minutes). Add milk and pimento, and heat to just below boiling. Make paste of arrowroot, curry powder and 2 tablespoons of water. Stir into peas and cook over low heat until thickened. Makes 2½ cups. Serve with any vegetable, grain, fish or chicken entree needing a sauce. ½ cup = 45 calories.

# Mornay Sauce

1 cup Chablis wine
1 cup skim milk
2 ounces shredded Jarlsberg
  cheese

2 tablespoons arrowroot
2 teaspoons herb seasoning

Place wine in a saucepan and bring to a boil; remove from flame. Combine arrowroot and herb seasoning with skim milk and add to heated wine. Add shredded Jarlsberg slowly, whipping with a wire whisk constantly until it is fully dissolved. I ounce serving = 20 calories.

# Tomato Sauce

16 ounces whole, peeled,
   unsalted, tomatoes
16 ounces unsalted tomato juice
1 small potato wrapped in gauze
1 teaspoon basil

1 teaspoon chopped parsley
½ teaspoon thyme
½ teaspoon marjoram
4 cracked bay leaves
1 clove of garlic, pressed

Combine tomatoes, tomato juice, spices and one potato wrapped in gauze (to absorb acidity) in a small pot. Bring mixture to a boil then reduce heat to simmer for 20 minutes. Discard potato. 2 ounce serving = 15 calories.

# Chicken Sauce

1 cup chicken consommé
4 teaspoons arrowroot

1 ounce skim milk

Bring stock to boil. Mix arrowroot with milk and add slowly to stock while whipping vigorously with a small wire whisk. Serving size = 2 ounces. 15 calories per 2 ounce serving.

# Spa Sauce

16 ounces whole, peeled,
    unsalted or fresh tomatoes
16 ounces unsalted tomato juice
1 teaspoon basil
1 teaspoon oregano
1 teaspoon chopped parsley
½ teaspoon thyme

½ teaspoon marjoram
4 cracked bay leaves
1 clove garlic, pressed
⅓ cup puréed celery
⅓ cup puréed onions
⅓ cup puréed carrots

Combine tomatoes, tomato juice, puréed vegetables and spices in a small pot. Bring mixture to a boil then reduce heat to simmer for 20 minutes. 2 ounce serving = 15 calories per serving.

# Bar-B-Q Sauce

½ cup tomato sauce or paste
    (low sodium)
½ cup crushed unsweetened
    pineapple, drained
1 teaspoon lemon juice

1 teaspoon onion flakes/powder
½ teaspoon garlic powder
¼ teaspoon pepper
1 teaspoon tabasco

Mix all ingredients thoroughly. Use on lean beef or chicken. Makes ¾ cup. 1 ounce = 15 calories.

# Cranberry Sauce

*1 cup clear apple juice*
*2 teaspoons arrowroot*

*1 cup fresh cranberries, cleaned*
*6 packages Equal*

Boil cranberries until tender and drain. Mix apple juice and arrowroot in small saucepan until lump-free. Add cranberries and cook, stirring constantly, over moderate heat until sauce clears and thickens. At end of cooking, add Equal and mix well. Makes 1½ cups. 1 ounce = 10 calories.

# Cocktail Sauce

*8 ounces low sodium tomato*
  *puree*
*2 ounces horseradish*

*2 tablespoons lemon juice*
*2 ounces unsweetened pineapple*
  *juice*

Mix all ingredients and chill well before serving. 2 ounce serving = 10 calories.

# Mustard Sauce

*¾ cup low calorie whipped*
  *dressing (D'Mayo or Weight*
  *Watchers)*

*¼ cup Dijon mustard*

Mix well and chill before serving. 1 tablespoon = 20 calories.

# Mock Sour Cream

No real cream is used in this mock sour cream, yet it is truly delicious. It tastes much like real sour cream, and may be used wherever real sour cream is used. Use it on baked potatoes, in salads, on pancakes, as a dip, etc.

*½ gallon skim milk*          *¼ cup cultured buttermilk*

Combine ingredients and heat slowly, stirring constantly. Cover, remove from heat, and let stand in a warm place until coagulated (1 or 2 days). Turn curd into colander lined with 4 layers of cheesecloth. Let drain until whey has drained through (4-6 hours). Stir and serve. Makes 2 cups. *For an excellent substitute for this sour cream, blend any of the 1% cottage cheeses on the market until smooth. 1 ounce = 40 calories.

# Blueberry Sauce

*1 cup clear apple juice*        *1 cup frozen whole blueberries*
*2 teaspoons arrowroot*         *(or any other berries)*

Mix apple juice and arrowroot in small saucepan until lump-free. Add blueberries and cook, stirring constantly, over moderate heat until sauce clears and thickens, mashing berries while stirring. Serve hot over pancakes. Makes 1½ cups. ½ cup = 50 calories.

Optional: When sauce is ready to serve, stir in additional ½ cup of frozen berries. Use this cooled sauce over pancakes or reheat slightly, stirring gently to avoid crushing berries.

# Crushed Raspberry Applesauce

*1 cup raspberries*
*2 cups applesauce*

*½ ounce sliced unblanched*
*almonds, toasted*

In small bowl, mash raspberries with fork. Add applesauce; stir well to blend. Spoon evenly into 4 dessert dishes; sprinkle evenly with almonds. Makes 4 servings. 80 calories.

# Provençale Sauce

*16 ounces whole, peeled,*
*unsalted or fresh tomatoes*
*16 ounces unsalted tomato juice*
*1 teaspoon basil*
*1 teaspoon oregano*
*1 teaspoon chopped parsley*
*½ teaspoon thyme*

*½ teaspoon marjoram*
*4 cracked bay leaves*
*1 clove garlic, pressed*
*⅓ cup puréed celery*
*⅓ cup puréed onions*
*⅓ cup puréed carrots*

Combine tomatoes, tomato juice, puréed vegetables and spices in a small pot. Bring mixture to a boil then reduce heat to simmer for 20 minutes. 2 ounce serving = 15 calories.

# VEGETABLES

## Steamed Mixed Vegetables

*½ cup of any combination of
the following vegetables:
Broccoli
Summer squash
Green beans
Cauliflower
Carrot*

*½ cup low sodium CHICKEN
STOCK
Basil, lemon juice or Mrs. Dash*

Season stock with basil, lemon juice or Mrs. Dash to enhance flavor. Steam vegetables in stock until soft but still crunchy. 1 cup serving = 40 calories.

## Mixed Greens

*½ pound spinach, washed and
chopped
½ pound Swiss chard, washed
and chopped*

*3 sprigs parsley, chopped
2 large green onion bottoms,
chopped
¼ teaspoon Italian seasoning*

Combine still-wet vegetables and seasoning in pot. Adding no water, cover tightly and cook 5 to 10 minutes over low heat. Serve hot. Serves 4. 1 cup = 35 calories.

# Carrots with Pineapple

Neither carrots nor pineapple ever tasted so good. This sweet and delicious recipe comes from a Hindu Ashram in Boston. Use it as a side dish when serving pastas, bean dishes or meat dishes.

4 medium carrots, peeled
   diagonally sliced (¼ inch slices)
1 28 ounce can of juice-packed,
   unsweetened crushed pineapple (room temperature)

⅛ teaspoon ginger

Place carrots in a sauce pan and add juice from canned pineapple. (Add additional pineapple juice or water, if necessary, to cover carrots.) Cover, boil gently until carrots are tender (about 20 minutes), and drain. Stir in crushed pineapple and ginger. Serves 4. ½ cup = 50 calories.

# Mixed Vegetables

Use any vegetables you wish to make a delicious mixed vegetable dish. Here is a favorite combination.

1 medium potato (⅓ pound),
   diced
1 cup cauliflower, separated into
   flowerets

1 cup broccoli, cut into small
   pieces
1 cup summer squash, sliced

Steam vegetables until tender. Serve plain or with SPAGHETTI SAUCE. Makes 5 cups. 1 cup = 56 calories (without sauce).

# Cauliflower in Bloom

1 head cauliflower
2 bunches broccoli
2 lemons, cut in lengthwise
  wedges

Thyme
Savory

Cut out green stem and pulpy center of cauliflower. Rinse. Cut off the inedible bottom parts of the broccoli stems and wash broccoli. Place a vegetable steaming rack at the bottom of large pot and add water just to the level of the rack bottom. Place cauliflower and broccoli in rack, add spices to taste, cover pot tightly and steam until tender (about 20 minutes). Serve on a large platter with cauliflower in center and broccoli groups radiating outward, interspersed with lemon wedges. Makes 6 servings. 1 cup = 30 calories.

# Beans and Spinach

16 ounces white or red kidney
  beans, cooked
2 packages frozen spinach,
  cooked
4-5 celery stalks (inner ones
  preferred), diced

½ clove garlic (more if you
  dare!), minced
¼ teaspoon crushed red pepper
¼ teaspoon oregano
¼ teaspoon parsley

Sauté garlic and celery in pan sprayed with non-caloric vegetable spray. When tender, add beans, sprinkle spices over mixture and toss with spinach. Heat thoroughly and serve. Serves 8. 1 serving = 75 calories.

# Broccoli Souffle

2 cups cooked broccoli, drained
   and finely chopped
¼ teaspoon nutmeg
¼ cup egg whites

¼ cup evaporated skim milk
Pepper and other seasonings to
   taste

Season broccoli with nutmeg, pepper and other seasonings if desired. Fold in milk and egg whites. Place in 1 quart casserole. Bake at 400 degrees about 20 minutes. Serves 4. ½ cup = 45 calories.

# Pickled Beets

4 medium beets, sliced and
   cooked
⅔ cup cooking liquid from beets
½ medium onion, sliced

2 tablespoons vinegar
10 peppercorns
6 whole, dried cloves
2 dozen mustard seeds

Combine all ingredients and marinate in refrigerator 24 hours. Makes 3 cups. 1 cup = 35 calories.

# Great Northern Beans

8 ounces cooked, dried beans
1 teaspoon dehydrated onion
  flakes
1 garlic clove crushed (or garlic
  powder)

1 medium tomato, chopped
½ cup sliced carrots

Place all ingredients in a heavy pot or skillet and heat thoroughly, at least 40 minutes. Stir every once in awhile so all ingredients mix. Serves 3. 1 serving = 150 calories.

# Brussels Sprouts with Walnuts

2 cups fresh brussels sprouts
1 tablespoon diet margarine

¼ cup chopped walnuts
¼ teaspoon ground nutmeg

Cut the brussels sprouts in half and steam them until tender. Meanwhile, sauté the walnuts in the margarine until golden. Pour walnuts over the sprouts in a serving dish. Sprinkle on the nutmeg. Makes 4 servings. 1 serving = ¼ of recipe. 100 calories.

# Zucchini and Tomato Sauce

*1 tablespoon olive oil*
*½ cup chopped onion*
*1 garlic clove, minced*
*3 cups zucchini chunks*
*½ teaspoon dried thyme, crushed*

*1 bay leaf*
*5 large plum tomatoes, cut into*
 *chunks*
*Fresh ground pepper*

In heavy large nonstick skillet, over high heat, heat oil. Add onion and garlic; sauté 5 minutes. Add thyme and bay leaf, cook one minute. Add zucchini and cook, stirring frequently, 4-5 minutes until tender. Add tomatoes and cook, stirring frequently, until heated through but still firm. Season to taste with pepper. Remove and discard bay leaf before serving. Makes 4 servings. 80 calories per serving.

| VEGETABLE | AMOUNT TO PURCHASE FOR 4 SERVINGS | SELECTION | PREPARATION | COOKING TIME (min) Boil | Steam | Bake |
|---|---|---|---|---|---|---|
| Artichokes | 2 lb. | Choose compact, heavy plump globes with large tightly clinging leaf scalels of olive green color. Size is not an important quality factor in choosing artichokes. | Cut off stems. Pull off tough bottom row of leaves and cut off ¼ of tops. Use scissors. | 35-45 | | |
| Asparagus | 1½ bunches or 1 lb. | Spears should be fresh and firm with compact closed tips. Select spears with large amount of green. | Cut off tough part of stems. Cut into 1" pieces, or tie in a bundle. | 5-15 | 7-15 | |
| Beans, Fresh Lima | ⅘ lb. shelled or 1½ to 2½ lb. in pods. | | Shell if in pods. (Scald pods to make shelling easier.) | 20-40 | 25-40 | |
| Beans, Green | ⅘ lb.-1 lb. | Pods should be firm, crisp and slender with good green color. | Trim ends and remove strings. Cut or break. | 20-35 | 15-30 | |
| Beets, Young Small Mature | 1 to 1½ bunches 1 to 1¼ lb. | | Remove tops, leave 2" stem on beets. Do not peel or remove root until cooked. | 30-45 | 40-60 | 40-60 |
| Beet greens | 1 to 1½ lb. | Choose fresh, young and crisp green leaves. Avoid any with coarse stems or wilted leaves. | Cut off tough stems. Wash at least 5 times, lifting out of water after each washing. | 5-15 | | |
| Broccoli | 1 to 1½ lb. | Look for compact bud clusters. Color varies from dark green, sage green or purplish-green depending on variety. Yellow and wilted leaves indicate aging. | Cut off stalk and ends. Soak in salted water ½ hr. if insects are present. Drain. Peel stalks. Cut lengthwise if thick. | 8-20 | 15-20 | |
| Brussels Sprouts | ⅘ to 1 lb. | Should be firm, compact and with bright leaves. Avoid wilted or yellow leaves. | Remove wilted leaves. | 6-15 | 8-18 | |
| Cabbage | 1 lb. | Heads should be reasonably solid and heavy in relation to size, with green outer leaves (except red cabbage). | Remove wilted outer leaves. Quarter and core. Crisp in cold water if wilted. Cut in wedges or shred. | 12-15 | 15 | |

| VEGETABLE | AMOUNT TO PURCHASE FOR 4 SERVINGS | SELECTION | PREPARATION | COOKING TIME (min) Boil | Steam | Bake |
|---|---|---|---|---|---|---|
| Carrots, Old Young | ¾ to 1 lb. 1 to 1½ bunches | Look for firm, well shaped roots with a good orange color. | Scrape or pare. Trim ends. Cut as desired. | 15-20 | 20-25 | |
| Cauliflower Whole Flowerets | 1¾ to 2 lb. | White or creamy white, firm, compact curds indicate good quality. | Remove outer leaves and stalks. Soak in water to draw out any insects present. | 20-30 8-15 | 25-30 10-15 | |
| Celery | 1 bunch or 1 lb. | Choose fresh, crisp stalks that are thick and solid with good heart formation. | Trim, cut as desired. | 15-20 | 25-30 | |
| Collards | 2 lb. | | Sort and trim. Strip leaves from coarse stems. Wash at least 5 times, lifting out of water after each wash. | 10-20 | | |
| Corn | 4 ears | Select only corn that is cold to the touch. Husks should be green, not dry or yellowish. | Husk and remove silks. Do not allow to stand in water. | 5-10 | 10-15 | |
| Cucumbers | 3 medium | Look for medium sizes with good green color. Avoid very large, puffy ones or any having a yellow color. | Can be pared or eaten with skin. | 5-10 | | |
| Eggplant | 1 medium | Should be firm and heavy for their size, with dark purple to purple-black skin. | Peel and cut into slices or pieces. | 8-15 | 12-20 | |
| Mustard Greens | 1½ to 2 lb. | Choose fresh, young and crisp green leaves. Avoid any with coarse stems or wilted leaves. | Cut off tough stems. Wash at least 5 times, lifting out of water after each wash. | 15-25 | | |
| Okra | 1 lb. | Pods should be young and tender, preferably 2″ to 4″ long. Avoid dull, dry or shriveled pods. | Trim stem. Slice or leave whole. | 10-20 | 20 | |

# VEGETABLES

| VEGETABLE | AMOUNT TO PURCHASE FOR 4 SERVINGS | SELECTION | PREPARATION | COOKING TIME (min) Boil | Steam | Bake |
|---|---|---|---|---|---|---|
| Onions, Large Small | 1 lb. | Should be clean and firm. Skins should be dry, smooth and crackly. Avoid onions with wet, soggy necks, soft or spongy bulbs. Keep at room temperature, cool. May be stored 3-4 weeks. | Trim stem. Slice or leave whole. | 20-35 15-25 | 45-60 30-50 | |
| Parsnips | 1 lb. | Smooth, firm, well shaped of small to medium size. Discoloration may be a sign of freezing. | Pare. Cut core from center if tough and woody. | 15-25 | 30-40 | |
| Peas | 1½ to 2 lb. in pods. | | Shell. Rinse. | 8-20 | 10-20 | |
| Potatoes, White | 1 to 1½ lb. | Choose firm, clean and relatively smooth, free from cuts or bruises. Avoid green colored ones and those with sprouts. Never refrigerate, but keep in a cool, dark area. | Scrub. Cook in skins or pare and cut into serving size. Cover with cold water to prevent darkening. Prolonged soaking causes loss of nutrients. | 25-35 | 30-45 | 45-60 |
| Pumpkin | 1½ to 2 lb. | | Cut in half. Remove seeds, fiber and peel. Cut in pieces. (If peel is hard and tough, soften by steaming or boiling 10 minutes.) | 20-25 | 25-30 | |
| Rutabagas | 1¼ | Should be firm, heavy for its size, smooth and not deeply cut or punctured. Size is not a quality factor. | Pare and cut as desired. | 20-30 | | |
| Spinach | 1½ to 2 lb. | Leaves should be clean and fresh, of a dark green color. Avoid any with large yellow leaves or those which are wilted or discolored. | Sort and trim. Cut off coarse stems and roots. Wash at least 5 times, lifting out of water after each washing. | 3-5 | 5-10 | |

| VEGETABLE | AMOUNT TO PURCHASE FOR 4 SERVINGS | SELECTION | PREPARATION | COOKING TIME (min) Boil | Steam | Bake |
|---|---|---|---|---|---|---|
| Squash, Summer | 1½ to 2 lb. | Should be fresh, heavy for its size and tender. Choose small to medium sizes. Refrigerate, use as soon as possible. | Trim and cut as desired. | 5-15 | 15-20 | 30 |
| Squash, Winter | 1½ to 2 lb. | Avoid any with soft areas. Well adapted to long storage periods. Hubbards can be stored 6 months, acorn squash 3-6 months. Store in well ventilated area at room temp. | Cut in half, remove seeds, fiber and peel. Dice. If peel is hard and tough, soften by steaming or boiling 10 minutes. | 25-30 | 30-40 | |
| Turnips | 1 lb. | Should be firm, smooth, of medium size. Avoid yellowed or wilted tops, which indicate old age. | Pare and cut as desired. | 10-20 | 20-25 | |
| Turnip Greens | 1½ to 2 lb. | Choose fresh, young and crisp green leaves. Avoid any with coarse stems or wilted, yellow leaves. | Sort. Cut off tough stems. Wash at least 5 times, lifting out of water after each washing. | 15-20 | | |
| Zucchini | 1½ to 2 lb. | Should be fresh, heavy for its size and tender. Choose small to medium sizes. Refrigerate and use as soon as possible. | Trim and cut as desired. | 5-15 | 15-20 | 30 |

# SIDE DISHES

## Orange Chicken Salad Sandwich

2 6-inch whole wheat pita bread
8 ounces cubed chicken breast
2 tablespoons whipped dressing
1 mandarin orange

½ cup chopped celery
1 teaspoon herb seasonings

Combine all ingredients in a mixing bowl. Slice 6-inch whole wheat pita bread into two equal halves. Stuff 4 pita halves evenly with chicken salad. Garnish with shredded lettuce and slice of tomato. Makes 4 servings. 180 calories per serving.

## Tuna Salad Sandwich in Pita Bread

3 ounces canned white tuna
  (in water)
1 tablespoon low calorie salad
  dressing

½ cup chopped celery, onion,
  and carrot
½ pita bread

Mix all ingredients together and place in pita bread pocket. Serve with a lettuce leaf and a slice of tomato. 175 calories.

# Eggless Salad Sandwich

1 cup liquid egg whites
5 tablespoons low calorie, lowfat,
  low sodium mayonnaise
2 tablespoons minced celery
2 tablespoons minced green
  pepper

1 teaspoon minced onion
½ teaspoon prepared mustard
Add pepper to taste (optional)
Dash red pepper sauce, or pinch
  red pepper (optional)

Cook egg whites covered in non-stick skillet over very low heat about 10 to 15 minutes, or until the egg whites thicken and are set. Remove from heat and cool slightly. Dice or shred the cooked egg whites; combine with remaining ingredients. Chill. 80 calories.

# Toasted Turkey and Cheese Sandwich

1 ounce (2 slices) of low fat
  Jarlsberg cheese
2 slices whole wheat bread
Vegetable coating spray (Pam)

2 ounces sliced roast turkey
  breast
¼ cup egg whites

Place one slice of cheese on one slice of bread. Top with turkey, second slice of cheese and bread. Place the sandwich in a shallow dish with the egg. Turn frequently until all the egg is absorbed and both sides are well coated. Spray non-stick skillet with cooking spray. Heat over moderate heat. Place sandwich on skillet; cook, turning once, until bread is browned and cheese is melted. 300 calories.

# Scalloped Potatoes with Vegetables

6 tablespoons skim milk
4 medium potatoes, cooked,
  cooled and peeled
½ cup cooked peas
½ cup cooked cauliflower pieces
½ cup cooked, chopped celery

¼ cup cooked, diced carrots
½ cup WHITE SAUCE
¼ teaspoon tumeric
1 tablespoon parsley flakes
Matzo meal
Paprika

Pour half of the skim milk into bottom of rectangular baking dish. Slice 2 potatoes, and layer into dish. Mix peas, cauliflower, celery, carrots, white sauce and spices and place this mixture as a layer over the potatoes. Slice remaining two potatoes as a top layer, pour rest of milk over top, sprinkle with matzo meal and paprika and bake at 400 degrees until top is browned and casserole is not. Serves 6. 1 serving = 100 calories.

# Company Potatoes

4 large potatoes
¼ cup parsley flakes
¾ cup chopped onions
4 cloves garlic, finely chopped
¼ teaspoon caraway seeds

2 cups MOCK SOUR CREAM
2 egg whites
¼ teaspoon dill weed
1 teaspoon pepper

Peel, slice, and boil the potatoes with half of the parsley flakes. Drain, combine with all remaining ingredients, and mix with electric mixer to the consistency of thick mashed potatoes. Spread mixture over bottom of shallow casserole dish, sprinkle bread or cracker crumbs over top if desired and bake ½ hour at 350 degrees. Serves 8. 1 serving = 150 calories.

# Confetti Rice

1½ pounds zucchini sliced
¾ cup onion, diced
1 17 ounce can of corn, no salt
  added
1 16 ounce can of tomatoes, no
  salt added, drained

3 cups cooked brown rice
½ teaspoon garlic powder
¼ teaspoon pepper
¼ teaspoon parsley
¼ teaspoon oregano
Vegetable coating spray (Pam)

Sauté zucchini and onion with seasonings in a non-stick pan
(spray with Pam). Combine with other ingredients and simmer
15 minutes. Serves 6. 1 serving = 150 calories.

# Wild Rice Chicken Stuffing

½ cup wild rice, rinsed
1 tablespoon regular non-fat dry
  milk
1 tablespoon parsley flakes

3 egg whites
⅛ teaspoon pepper
¾ cup low sodium, low fat
  cottage cheese

Place rice in small saucepan, add 2 cups water, cover and
simmer 35 minutes. Drain rice thoroughly. Combine dry milk,
parsley flakes, egg whites and pepper, crushing lumps of milk
to make smooth. Stir in cheese and rice. Makes 2½ cups. ½ cup
serving = 65 calories.

# Appled Rice

*1 cup brown rice*
*½ cup wild rice*
*2 medium apples*

*1 tablespoon lemon juice*
*⅛ teaspoon cardamom*

Bring one quart of water to a boil in open pressure cooker. Add rice and cook under 15 pounds of pressure for 10 minutes. (For rocking-cap type cooker, cook for 10 minutes after pressure cap begins rocking). Remove from heat and allow pressure to drop by itself. Peel, core and finely chop apples into lemon juice, stirring to coat. Stir apples and cardamom into rice, cover, let sit 5 minutes and serve. Serves 8. 1 serving = 85 calories.

# Fiber Dressing (Stuffing)

*2 egg whites*
*2 slices of whole wheat bread,*
  *diced*
*½ cup of diced celery*
*½ cup shredded carrot*
*½ cup sliced mushrooms*

*½ cup diced onion*
*½ cup chicken consommé*
*1 clove garlic, pressed*
*½ teaspoon herb seasoning*
*Vegetable coating spray (Pam)*

Steam vegetables and seasonings in chicken consommé for 8-10 minutes. Remove vegetables and combine with egg whites and diced bread. Place in a small baking pan, lightly sprayed with vegetable oil and bake in 350 degree oven for 20 minutes. Makes 4 servings = 2 ounces each. 50 calories per serving.

# Stove Potatoes

5 medium potatoes, peeled and
  diced
1 large onion, diced

1 tablespoon parsley flakes
½ teaspoon pepper

Combine all ingredients in saucepan, add enough water to cover and cook over medium flame until tender (about 20 minutes). Drain and serve. So good and so easy to fix. Serves 4. 1 cup = 120 calories.

# Quick Tortilla Chips

6 corn tortillas
Onion powder to taste

Garlic powder to taste

Preheat oven to 400 degrees. Cut each tortilla into eight triangles. Place triangles on cake rack and bake 6 minutes. Turn chips over, sprinkle with garlic, onion or both. Bake 3 minutes more. Makes 48 chips (a nice bowlful). Use with any dip. Goes especially well with CHILI SALSA. 16 chips = 128 calories.

# VEGETARIAN ENTREES

## Vegetable Lasagna

2 cups cooked lasagna
½ cup steamed cauliflower
½ cup steamed zucchini
½ cup steamed broccoli
½ cup steamed summer squash
½ cup diced onions
12 ounces low sodium tomato
  sauce

4 ounces part skim ricotta cheese
2 ounces part skim mozzarella
  cheese
Vegetable coating spray (Pam)
½ cup diced green pepper
½ cup sliced mushrooms

Cook lasagna according to package directions until "al dente," soft but still firm. Spray a medium size frying pan with Pam, heat, and add onions and sauté until transparent. Add green peppers and mushrooms and sauté until tender. Pour in tomato sauce and simmer over a medium flame for 10 minutes. Spray a 6" × 6" baking pan with Pam, line bottom with one layer of lasagna noodles. Spread layer of vegetables evenly over the lasagna and top with tomato sauce. Then evenly distribute a layer of ricotta cheese over the vegetable-sauce mixture. Form a top layer with remaining lasagna noodles, spread mozzarella cheese over the lasagna and bake in 350 degree oven for 45 minutes. Serves 4. 175 calories.

# Manicotti

12 manicotti noodles (usually
   the contents of a single
   package)
3 cups low fat cottage cheese
3 egg whites
2 teaspoons parsley flakes

½ teaspoon thyme
½ teaspoon basil
½ teaspoon garlic powder
1 quart SPAGHETTI SAUCE
½ teaspoon pepper

Cook manicotti noodles to "al dente" stage. Drain and place in cool water while casserole is being made. Combine cottage cheese, egg whites and spices, adding a little water if necessary to optimize the mixture for stuffing. Spread a cup of the spaghetti sauce over the bottom of the baking dish. One by one, drain each noodle, stuff it with the cottage cheese mixture, using a long-handled spoon, and lay it in the baking dish. Pour remaining sauce over top and bake at 375 degrees until slightly browned on top (about 30 minutes). Serves 6. 2 manicotti noodles with sauce = 200 calories.

# Zucchini Lasagna

4 small zucchini squash peeled
   and sliced
4 cups low fat cottage cheese
1 cup egg whites (about 8 eggs)
¼ cup parsley flakes

½ teaspoon pepper
1 pound lasagna noodles, cooked
   "al dente" and drained
1 quart SPAGHETTI SAUCE

Cook zucchini 10 minutes in vegetable steamer. Make a cheese mixture by combining cottage cheese with egg whites, parsley and pepper. Layer ingredients as follows: noodles, cheese mixture, spaghetti sauce and zucchini, cheese mixture and spaghetti sauce. Repeat until all ingredients have been used. Bake 1 hour at 350 degrees. Serves 8. 1 serving = 200 calories.

# Spinach Lasagna

Who would think spinach would go so well in a lasagna dish?

2 bunches fresh spinach
1 pound lasagna noodles
2 small onions, chopped
½ cup sliced mushrooms
½ large green pepper, chopped
½ teaspoon minced garlic
3 cups low fat cottage cheese

2 egg whites
1 tablespoon parsley flakes
½ teaspoon pepper
Bread crumbs
1 28 ounce can tomatoes, with
    half the liquid in the can
    (low sodium)

PREPARE SPINACH:
Wash leaves thoroughly and remove stems; wilt spinach by placing in the colander and then plunging in hot water for 10 seconds; chop wilted spinach finely.

PREPARE NOODLES:
Cook and drain.

PREPARE SAUCE:
Saute onions, mushrooms, green pepper and garlic in three tablespoons water, add the canned tomatoes and juice after chopping 2 or 3 seconds in the blender; add spices and simmer 30 minutes, then add spinach.

PREPARE CHEESE MIXTURE:
Mix cottage cheese with egg whites, then add parsley flakes and pepper.

PREPARE LASAGNA FOR BAKING:
Place ⅓ of the noodles in the bottom of a baking dish 9″ × 13″ × 2″; layer in ⅓ of the cheese mixture, followed by ⅓ of sauce; repeat process twice more, using up all the noodles, cheese mixture and sauce. Top with bread crumbs and bake at 350 degrees for about 30 minutes. Serves 10. 1 serving = 200 calories.

# Fettucini Marco

2 cups cooked fettucini
4 ounces part skim ricotta cheese
4 tablespoons grated Parmesan
   cheese

8 ounces unflavored non-fat
   yogurt
4 egg whites

Cook fettucini in a large pot of boiling water until it is "al dente," soft but still firm. Strain the cooked fettucini and run under cold water. Using an electric mixer, whip ricotta cheese, egg whites and yogurt together until smooth. Combine this mixture with the fettucini in a small casserole dish and sprinkle Parmesan cheese on top. Bake at 325 degrees for 15 minutes. Cut into four equal portions, garnish with a sprig of parsley and serve hot. 1 serving = 175 calories.

# Eggplant Parmesan

1 pound of eggplant, sliced
   thin
4 ounces part skim mozzarella
   cheese, grated

8 ounces low sodium tomato
   sauce, heated
Vegetable coating spray (Pam)
2 cups cooked brown rice

Divide mozzarella into 4 one ounce slices. Lightly spray a small frying pan with Pam and sauté eggplant over a medium flame. Combine cooked eggplant with grated mozzarella, place in a lightly sprayed baking pan and bake in 350 degree oven for five minutes. Remove from oven, cover each of the four eggplant servings with 2 ounces of warm tomato sauce and serve with ½ cup rice. 175 calories. EGGPLANT PROVENCALE: Omit cheese in Eggplant Parmesan. 1 serving = 100 calories.

# Stuffed Zucchini with Fiber Dressing

2 zucchinis                              Vegetable coating spray (Pam)
FIBER DRESSING

Cut zucchinis in half lengthwise and scoop out centers. Stuff each with 2 ounces of fiber dressing, place in a baking pan lightly sprayed with Pam and bake in a 350 degree oven for 20 minutes. Serves 2. 175 calories.

## FIBER DRESSING

2 egg whites
4 slices whole grain bread,
   diced
½ cup diced celery
½ cup diced onion
½ cup diced carrots
1 clove garlic, pressed

½ cup fresh finely chopped
   mushrooms
1 teaspoon parsley
½ cup low sodium chicken
   consommé
½ teaspoon herb seasoning

Steam vegetables and seasonings in chicken consommé for 8 to 10 minutes. Remove and combine with egg whites and diced bread. Mix until all ingredients are evenly blended.

# Nada's Vegetarian Cabbage Rolls

*1 large head cabbage*

## STUFFING

*2 cups cooked and drained red, kidney or garbanzo beans or any combination*
*1 cup chopped onion*
*1 cup diced celery*
*½ cup partially cooked brown rice\**
*1 cup tomato sauce (low sodium)*

*1 16 ounce can whole tomatoes drained, cropped finely*
*1 tablespoon parsley flakes*
*½ teaspoon garlic flakes*
*¼ teaspoon oregano flakes*
*⅛ teaspoon pepper*
*1 egg white*

## SAUCE

*1 28 ounce can tomatoes packed in purée, low sodium (blended 5 seconds in blender)*

*1 tablespoon parsley flakes*
*1 stalk celery, diced*
*⅛ teaspoon garlic flakes*

Place whole cabbage in a large pot, add 1 cup water, cover tightly, and steam until cabbage leaves can be separated (about 20 minutes). Mix all stuffing ingredients together. On each cabbage leaf, place a small amount of stuffing (about 3 table-spoons), tuck in ends, roll up and place in shallow baking dish. Largest leaves may be cut in half to keep rolls more or less uniform in size. Combine sauce ingredients. Chop unused center of cabbage and add ½ cup of this chopped cabbage to sauce. Pour sauce over cabbage rolls, cover and bake 25 minutes at 350 degrees. Remove cover and bake 20 minutes more. Makes about 16 rolls. Serves 8. 1 cabbage roll = 60 calories.

*To partially cook, boil vigorously 10 minutes in 1½ cups water, drain.

# Green Bean Casserole

*1½ pounds fresh green beans*
*¼ teaspoon pepper*
*1½ cups low fat cottage cheese*

*2 cups VERSATILITY SAUCE*
*1 tablespoon CHILI SALSA (or
    more to taste)*

## TOPPINGS
*¼ cup fresh bread crumbs or 3 hard-cooked egg whites, shredded*

Simmer green beans, covered, in ½ cup water for 20 minutes. Drain. Combine green beans, pepper, Chili Salsa and cheese in shallow glass baking dish. Pour sauce over all, top with either or both toppings and bake at 350 degrees until surface browns (about 20 minutes). Serves 6. 1 cup = 75 calories.

# Mushroom and Potato Garden

4 large potatoes, suitable for
   baking
1½ cups MOCK SOUR
   CREAM or low fat cottage
   cheese
½ pound fresh mushrooms,
   sliced

1 teaspoon garlic juice
1 teaspoon onion juice
1½ cups alfalfa sprouts
3 medium tomatoes, cut into
   wedges
1 green pepper, sliced

Wash potatoes and bake until done at 350 degrees (about 1 hour). Sauté mushrooms in garlic juice, onion juice, and 2 tablespoons water, until liquid is gone. Place each potato in center of individual serving plate, slit open, fill with sour cream or cottage cheese, and top with mushrooms. Surround each potato with heaps of sprouts. Symmetrically arrange tomato wedges and pepper slices around the potato, on top of the sprouts. Beautiful and delicious! Each potato arrangement is 1 serving. Serves 4.

*For large servings, use large (½ pound) potatoes = 220 calories per serving.

*For small servings, use medium (⅓ pound) potatoes = 150 calories per serving.

# Refried Beans

1½ cups dried pinto beans
  washed and picked over
1 teaspoon onion powder

2 tablespoons onion flakes
1 teaspoon pepper

Add beans slowly to 1½ quarts boiling water, making sure not to lose the boil. Reduce heat to medium, add spices, cover and cook just below boiling until beans are tender (about 1½ hours). Drain, mash beans, and stir and cook over medium-to-low flame until beans begin to look dry. Use refried beans in making burritos, tostados, and other Mexican dishes. Makes 1 quart. 1 cup = 240 calories.

# Tostados

REFRIED BEANS
Corn tortillas
Lettuce

Tomatoes
Onions
MOCK SOUR CREAM

Place tortillas on cookie sheet and place in a pre-heated 500 degree oven until crisp. Spread the crisp tortillas with the refried beans and top with lettuce, tomato, onions and mock sour cream. 1 tostado = 164 calories using ⅓ cup beans. 1 tostado = 203 calories using ½ cup beans.

# Enchiladas

This is a truly excellent vegetarian enchilada dish.

*18 Corn Tortillas*

## SAUCE

*4 cups tomato sauce (low
  sodium)*
*2-4 tablespoons CHILI SALSA
  (or any acceptable commer-
  cial salsa)*

*1 tablespoon parsley flakes*
*1 teaspoon vinegar*

## FILLING

*4 cups drained CHILI BEANS
  (reserve liquid)*
*½ cup liquid from chili beans*

*1 medium onion, chopped*
*1½ cups low fat cottage cheese*
*1 4 ounce can chopped mushrooms*

## TOPPING

*1 cup MOCK SOUR CREAM or low fat cottage cheese*

Combine all sauce ingredients and heat through, over low flame. Combine all filling ingredients, except cottage cheese, in saucepan and cook over medium heat 20 minutes. Add the cottage cheese and cook 5 minutes more. In a Teflon pan heat each tortilla on both sides until soft and pliable. Place 2 or 3 tablespoons of filling in the center of each tortilla, roll up and place in a glass baking dish 11" × 14" × 2". Continue until all filling is used. Pour sauce over enchiladas and top with sour cream or cottage cheese. Bake at 350 degrees for 20 minutes. Serves 6. 1 enchilada = 120 calories.

# Falafels

4 cups cooked garbanzos
4 egg whites
1 cup finely chopped onions
2 teaspoons chopped parsley
½ teaspoon garlic powder
¾ cup matzo meal (Manischewitz
  unsalted)

¼ cup potato pancake mix
  (Manischewitz)
½ teaspoon basil
Pepper

Put garbanzos and small amount of the cooking liquid in the blender. Blend until smooth. Mix the garbanzos, egg whites, onions and spices in a large bowl. Add sufficient matzo meal and pancake mix to make stiff enough to form small balls (about 1" inch). Bake on Teflon pan at 350 degrees for 15-20 minutes. Serve in pita bread: 3 to 4 balls to half a pita. Top with lettuce, tomato and onions. If desired, top with BUTTERMILK SPRING DRESSING or a mixture of tomato sauce and a small bit of prepared mustard. GAZPACHO also makes a great topping. 1 falafel (½ pita with 3 balls plus stuffing) = 150 calories.

# Vegetarian Pizza

4 slices French Bread 4" long
  by 2" thick
4 ounces low fat mozzarella
  cheese (shredded)

2 cups chopped green pepper,
  mushroom and onion
8 ounces MARINARA SAUCE

## MARINARA SAUCE

¼ cup low sodium chicken broth
1 small onion diced
1 clove garlic, crushed
¾ cup tomato sauce, low sodium

1 teaspoon dry mustard
4 tablespoons lemon juice
½ teaspoon chopped oregano
½ teaspoon chopped parsley

Combine all marinara sauce ingredients in saucepan, simmer 20 minutes, uncovered. Place 2 ounces marinara sauce on top of french bread and add ½ cup chopped vegetables and 1 ounce mozzarella cheese. Put in broiler until cheese melts. Recipe yields 4 servings. 175 calories includes slice of french bread, 1 ounce mozzarella cheese, 2 ounces MARINARA SAUCE, ½ cup chopped vegetables.

# Ranch Beans

2 pounds beans (red, pinto,
  kidney, etc. your choice)
1 jar chopped pimentos
½ pound fresh mushrooms,
  sliced

1 teaspoon garlic powder
2 tablespoons parsley flakes
½ teaspoon black pepper
1 large onion, diced

Pick over and rinse beans. Add beans slowly to 6 quarts boiling water. Return to boil. Add remaining ingredients. Simmer 2 hours or until tender. Makes 4-6 quarts. 1 cup = 50 calories.

*Additional bean recipes appear in the Appetizer and Soup Recipe Sections.*

# Stuffed Green Pepper with Jarlsberg Cheese

2 large green peppers
2 cups steamed rice
½ cup sautéed mushrooms
½ cup sautéed onions

4 ounces grated Jarlsberg Cheese
8 ounces tomato sauce (low sodium)
Vegetable coating spray (Pam)

Cut green pepper lengthwise and remove seeds. Steam for 3 minutes. Remove and run under cold water. Lightly spray a small frying pan with vegetable oil and place on a medium flame with the onions. Sauté onion until transparent and then add mushrooms. Once mushrooms are tender, add the tomato sauce and steamed rice to the frying pan and reduce heat to simmer. Simmer for 5 minutes, stirring occasionally. Fill each pepper with equal amounts of rice mixture. Place one ounce of Jarlsberg cheese on top and bake in 350 degree oven for 5 minutes. Makes 4 servings. 175 calories per serving.

# Garden Casserole

1 medium onion, chopped
1 teaspoon chili powder
1 teaspoon oregano
⅛ teaspoon ground cumin
Dash of cayenne pepper
1 medium green pepper, cut in strips

2 large zucchinis, sliced
1 cup corn kernels, fresh off the cob preferably
2 medium tomatoes, sliced
½ cup tiny sourdough bread cubes
Paprika

Place onion, spices and ¾ cup water in small saucepan and heat to boiling. Pour into casserole dish, add peppers, zucchini and corn, cover and bake one hour at 350 degrees. Then stir in tomatoes, top with bread cubes, sprinkle with a bit of paprika and bake uncovered an additional 25 minutes. Serves 4. 1 serving = 80 calories.

# Pasta E. Fagioli

2 cups cooked, drained pinto
  or red beans
½ pound flat noodles, cooked
1 16 ounce can low sodium
  tomato sauce
¼ ounce can low sodium tomato
  paste

1 clove garlic, minced
1 small onion, minced
½ green pepper, chopped
¼ teaspoon basil
⅛ teaspoon thyme
½ teaspoon parsley flakes

Prepare garlic, onion and pepper, and steam (3 to 5 minutes) until tender. Combine tomato sauce and paste and spices. Add steamed garlic, onion and pepper to sauce, add beans, and cook 20 minutes. Add cooked noodles and serve. Serves 4. 1 serving = 200 calories.

# Mushroom-Spinach Casserole

2 packages frozen spinach
½ cup chopped onions
2 tablespoons diet margarine,
  melted

1 pound fresh mushrooms
1 cup grated low fat Jarlsberg
  cheese
Garlic powder

Cook spinach according to directions, drain and line a shallow casserole with the spinach, which has been seasoned with onion, margarine, and garlic powder. Sprinkle with ½ cup cheese. Wash and dry mushrooms; arrange them, stem down over spinach. Season with more garlic powder and sprinkle with remaining cheese. Bake in 350 degree oven for 35 to 40 minutes. Serves 4 to 6. 1 serving = 100 calories.

# Tomatoes Stuffed with Spinach

4 medium tomatoes
1 package frozen chopped
   spinach thawed and drained
¼ cup shredded low fat skim
   mozzarella cheese

1 onion grated
1 cup low fat sour cream or
   plain non-fat yogurt
Pepper to taste (optional)

Cut tops from tomatoes. Scoop out center, leaving shells. Save pulp and drain tomatoes. Mix next four ingredients with tomato pulp; stuff mixture into shells. Place in shallow baking dish. Bake 20 to 25 minutes in 375 degree oven. Top with cheese and bake two to three minutes longer until cheese is melted. Serves 4. 1 serving = 100 calories.

# Baked Acorn Squash with Apples

5 large tart apples
½ cup firmly packed Sugar Twin
   brown sugar
¼ teaspoon cinnamon
½ cup grated sharp cheddar
   cheese

2 tablespoons lemon juice
¼ teaspoon nutmeg
3 medium size acorn squash
6 tablespoons diet margarine

Wash, peel, core and dice apples. Add to next five ingredients. Wash squash and cut in half lengthwise, scoop out insides. Fill centers with apple mixture. Top each with a tablespoon of margarine. Pour one inch water in shallow baking pan. Set squash in pan. Cover with foil and bake in 375 degree oven for one hour 15 minutes or until tender. Serves 6. 1 serving = ½ acorn = 200 calories.

# Veggie Stuffed Peppers

6 green peppers
2 cups cooked corn, drained
1 cup cooked lima beans, drained
¾ cup cooked black-eyed peas,
  drained
½ teaspoon garlic powder

¼ cup diet margarine
½ cup bacon bits (imitation)
2 slices stale whole wheat bread,
  crumbled
¼ teaspoon pepper

Cut off tops of peppers, remove seeds. Cook peppers 5 minutes in boiling water; drain and set aside. Combine remaining ingredients; stuff peppers. Place in shallow baking dish. Bake at 350 degrees for 10 minutes or until hot. Serves 6. 1 serving = 175 calories.

# Cheesy Stuffed Peppers

6 large green peppers
1 small onion chopped
¾ cup chopped celery
2 tablespoons diet margarine
2 medium tomatoes, chopped
2 cups cooked rice
¾ cup Jarlsberg cheese

¾ cup grated low fat mozzarella
  cheese
½ cup chopped almonds, toasted
½ cup whole wheat
¼ teaspoon pepper
Breadcrumbs (optional)

Cut off tops of peppers, remove seeds. Cook peppers 5 minutes in boiling water. Sauté onion and celery in a large skillet until tender. Add tomatoes and rice. Cook 15 minutes or until most of liquid is absorbed. Add remaining ingredients; mix quickly and stuff into peppers. Sprinkle top with breadcrumbs. Place in baking dish. Pour in 1 inch boiling water. Bake peppers at 350 degrees for 10 minutes. Serves 6. 1 serving = 300 calories.

# Rice-Cabbage Casserole

4 cups shredded cabbage
1 28 ounce can low sodium
   tomatoes, undrained and
   chopped
Garlic clove minced

1 tablespoon diet margarine
3 cups cooked brown rice
½ cup wheat cracker crumbs
½ cup shredded Jarlsberg cheese
½ cup chopped onion

Combine first five ingredients in a large saucepan; bring to a boil. Reduce heat, simmer 5 minutes. Place half of rice in Pam sprayed two quart casserole. Top with half of the cabbage mixture. Repeat layers. Mix cracker crumbs and cheese; sprinkle over casserole. Bake at 375 degrees for 45 minutes. Serves 8. 1 serving = 125 calories.

# Wild Rice Casserole

1 6 ounce package long grain
   and wild rice mix
6 green onions chopped
Vegetable coating spray (Pam)

8 medium mushrooms, sliced
2 cups CHICKEN BROTH
1 8 ounce can sliced water
   chestnuts, drained

Spray medium skillet with cooking spray. Place over medium heat until hot. Add rice; cook until lightly browned, stirring occasionally. Stir in remaining ingredients and spoon into a two quart casserole. Cover and bake at 350 degrees for one hour or until rice is done. 134 calories per serving. Serves 6.

# Cheesy Stuffed Eggplant

1 large eggplant
1 medium onion, chopped
1 garlic clove, minced
1 medium size green pepper,
  chopped
1 tablespoon vegetable oil
1 large tomato, peeled and
  chopped

2 tablespoons grated Parmesan
  cheese
⅓ cup sodium free tomato juice
½ cup sliced mushrooms
1 4 ounce pack low fat
  mozzarella cheese, shredded
1 teaspoon dried oregano
Pepper to taste

Wash eggplant and cut in half lengthwise. Remove pulp, leaving ¼ inch shell. Chop pulp and set aside. Sauté onion, pepper, and garlic in oil five minutes. Add chopped pulp, tomato, tomato juice and mushrooms. Cook over medium heat 15 to 20 minutes, stirring occasionally. Remove from heat. Stir in mozzarella, oregano, and black pepper. Place eggplant shells in shallow baking dish. Spoon mixture into shells, sprinkle with Parmesan cheese. Bake at 350 degrees for 20 minutes or until cheese melts. Serves 4. 1 serving = 175 calories.

# Stir Fry Vegetable Medley

4 *small zucchinis*
2 *large carrots*
2 *medium tomatoes cut up*
1 *package chinese peapods*
2 *cups chopped scallions*
1 *cup sliced mushrooms*
1 *cup slivered water chestnuts*

2 *garlic cloves minced*
½ *teaspoon oregano*
¼ *teaspoon basil (optional)*
2-3 *tablespoons toasted sesame seeds (optional)*
*Vegetable coating spray (Pam)*

Slice zucchini, carrots, water chestnuts in food processor. Spray vegetable coating spray in wok or large frying pan on high heat. Add carrots and sauté until just tender. Add zucchini and tomatoes, saute 2-3 minutes high temperature. Add next 7 ingredients, saute 2-3 minutes. Remove from heat. Sprinkle with sesame seeds. Serve immediately. Serves 6. 1 serving = 100 calories.

# Green Bean and Nut Casserole

1 *pound fresh green beans cooked lightly*
1 *pound bean sprouts*
½ *pound fresh mushrooms, sliced*
8 *ounce plain non-fat yogurt*

1 8½ *ounce can water chestnuts, sliced*
1 *cup sliced onions*
½ *cup low fat shredded Jarlsberg cheese*

Drain all Veggies and place in casserole with exception of cheese. Bake for 20 minutes in 400 degree oven. Sprinkle with cheese, bake 10 minutes more. Serves 8. 1 serving = 80 calories.

# Eggplant Casserole

1 large eggplant, sliced
Pepper and oregano to taste
3 tablespoons vegetable oil
1 cup chopped onion
2 garlic cloves minced

2 cups chopped fresh tomatoes
¼ cup chopped parsley
1 cup grated low fat Jarlsberg or
    low fat mozzarella cheese

Cut eggplant to steak size slices. Place in shallow pyrex pan sprayed with Pam. Brush lightly with oil. Sprinkle with pepper and oregano. Broil 5 minutes (tender but not mushy). Take remainder of oil, sautéed onion and garlic and heat on medium heat 2-3 minutes. Add tomatoes and parsley. Cook 5 minutes. Spoon over eggplant. Sprinkle top with cheese and broil 5 minutes more or until cheese is melted. Serves 4. 1 serving = 225 calories.

# Escarole and White Kidney Beans

2 heads escarole
1 8 ounces can Progresso
    cannellini beans, white kidney
    beans, undrained
2-3 stalks celery with leaves
    chopped fine

3 cloves garlic, minced
1 teaspoon dried oregano
1 tablespoon dried parsley
¼ teaspoon dried crushed red
    pepper
Vegetable coating spray (Pam)

Clean escarole well and cut in one inch pieces. Cook until tender. Do not add water to escarole, place in pot right from washing. It will make its own water. Sauté celery with vegetable coating spray until tender. Add next 4 ingredients. Sauté 2-3 minutes. Add beans with liquid they are packed in. Heat 2-3 minutes. Add bean mixture to cooked escarole. Do not drain escarole. Heat about 5 minutes, dish will be somewhat soupy but delicious! Serves 4. 1 serving = 75 calories.

# Stuffed Cheese Potato

1 baked potato
¼ cup low fat cottage
   cheese, chives, black pepper
   to taste

1 ounce low fat part skim
   mozzarella or Jarlsberg
   cheese shredded
Mrs. Dash (optional)

Cut baked potato in half, remove potato filling, add cottage cheese, chives and pepper (mixing well). Place filling into potato shells; add ½ ounce of shredded cheese on top of potato boats. Place boats into the broiler until cheese melts. Recipe yields 2 servings. 175 calories per serving.

# Chili and Macaroni

3 cups cooked pasta (shells,
   elbows, twists)
2 cups cooked Kidney beans
Chili powder to taste
Hot peppers and Tabasco (optional)

1 cup sautéed onions, green
   peppers and celery
1 cup SPA SAUCE

Mix all ingredients. Serve hot. May add hot peppers or Tabasco to recipe. Serves 4. 175 calories per serving.

# Black Beans and Rice

3 cups cooked brown rice
2 cups cooked black beans

1 cup sautéed onions, and celery
Chili powder—dash

## SAUCE

2 cups low sodium vegetable
  broth
Arrowroot—to slightly thicken

Onion and garlic powder to
  taste

Add sauce to cooked black beans, onions, and celery. Serve hot over brown rice. Serves 4. 175 calories per serving.

# Rice and Bean Stuffed Peppers

4 large peppers
2 cups cooked brown rice
1 cup cooked Kidney beans

4 cups marinara sauce (low
  sodium tomato puree, Mrs.
  Dash, garlic, oregano, pepper
  and low sodium crushed
  tomatoes)

Steam peppers until cooked but still firm. Cook marinara sauce. Mix together cooked rice, kidney beans then add 2 cups marinara sauce. Stuff peppers with rice and bean mixture. Place into a baking pan and add 2 cups of the marinara sauce over the stuffed peppers. Cook at 350 degrees for 15 minutes, then serve. Serves 4. 175 calories.

# Vegetable Quiche

*1 low fat pie crust*
*2 cups steamed mixed vegetables*
*3 ounces shredded Jarlsberg cheese*

*4 egg whites*
*6 ounces low fat cottage cheese*

Place steamed mixed vegetables into pie crust, mix both cheeses and blend into the vegetables. Beat egg whites, pour over pie. Bake at 350 degrees for 20 minutes or until golden brown on top. Cut pie into 6 pieces. ⅙ of pie = 200 calories. 1 pie serves 6.

# Spanish Brown Rice

*¾ cup brown rice*
*¾ cup chopped tomato*
*¼ cup chopped onion*
*¼ cup CHILI SALSA or other*
  *acceptable chili salsa.*

*¼ teaspoon cayenne pepper*
*⅓ teaspoon paprika*
*2 tablespoons chopped green*
  *pepper*
*Pinch of saffron*

In a saucepan combine all ingredients except rice. Add 2¼ cups water and bring to a boil. Add rice, return to a boil, cover and simmer one hour. Serves 4. 1 cup = 240 calories.

# SEAFOOD ENTREES

## Broiled Fish Fillets

1 pound tender-fleshed fish
  fillets (such as cod, whiting)
2 medium lemons
¼ teaspoon basil

⅛ teaspoon thyme
⅛ teaspoon pepper
¼ cup dry white wine
Fresh parsley sprigs

In a shallow pan, arrange fillets in a single layer. Brush or sprinkle fish with juice from one of the lemons, then sprinkle with basil, thyme and pepper. Pour wine into pan around (not on top of) fish. Broil close to heat until fish begins to brown and looks slightly dry, with juices congealing. Do not attempt to turn fish. Serve with parsley trim and wedges cut from remaining lemon. Serves 6. 1 serving = 100 calories.

# Fettucini with Seafood Marinara

16 ounces seafood (lobster
   meat, shrimp, scallops and
   crabmeat)
¼ cup low sodium chicken broth
1 small onion, diced
¾ cup tomato sauce (low
   sodium)

1 teaspoon dry mustard
4 tablespoons lemon juice
½ teaspoon chopped oregano
1 clove garlic, crushed
2 cups cooked fettucini

Combine all ingredients except seafood mixture in saucepan;
simmer 20 minutes uncovered. Place sauce over seafood and
marinate in refrigerator for at least one hour. Broil for 8 to 12
minutes, turning occasionally and brushing frequently with the
sauce. Do not overcook. Serve on ½ cup fettucini. Serves four.
One serving = 175 calories.

# Herbed Baked Fish Fillets

1 to 1½ pounds fish fillets
½ cup whole wheat flour
½ teaspoon garlic powder
1 egg white

½ teaspoon oregano
1 teaspoon freshly grated ginger
½ cup plain non-fat yogurt

Combine flour and herbs. Dip fish in egg white, then in flour
mixture. Place fish in single layer in baking pan. Spoon yogurt
over the fillets. Bake in pre-heated 400 degree oven for 15
minutes. Serves 4. 1 serving with ½ cup rice = 175 calories.

# Briny Deep Salmon Loaf

1 7¾ ounce can of salmon,
  rinsed and drained
3 cups soft bread crumbs
3 egg whites
½ cup skim milk

½ cup chopped onion
2 tablespoons parsley flakes
½ teaspoon tarragon
2½ cups CURRIED PEA
  SAUCE

Combine all ingredients except pea sauce, mixing and mashing well to distribute salmon, seasonings and wet ingredients thoroughly in bread crumbs. Shape mixture in a 8" × 8" × 2" Teflon pan. Bake 25 minutes at 400 degrees. Pour hot curried pea sauce over entire surface of salmon loaf and serve. Serves 4. ⅔ cup = 179 calories.

# Lobster Pernod

4 6 ounce lobster tails (with
  shell)

1 tablespoon Pernod
4 tablespoons skim milk

Slice each tail in half and drape meat over shell. Combine Pernod with skim milk and moisten each tail with 1 tablespoon of mixture. Place tails in a small roasting pan partially filled with water. Cover roasting pan with aluminum foil and bake in pre-heated 350 degree oven for 8-10 minutes. Makes 4 servings. 165 calories.

# Seafood Creole à la Pomme

4 medium potatoes
4 ounces scallops
4 ounces shrimp
2 ounces shredded Jarlsberg
  cheese
8 ounces tomato sauce, low
  sodium

½ cup chopped green peppers
½ medium onion, diced
½ cup mushrooms, sliced
Vegetable coating spray (Pam)

Bake potatoes at 425 degrees for 60 minutes. Remove potatoes from oven and let cool. Slice an elongated strip from the top portion of each potato. Take out the "meat" of the potato without piercing the skin. Set skins aside. Sauté onion in a lightly sprayed frying pan until transparent. Add green peppers and mushrooms and sauté. Pour in tomato sauce and seafood and simmer for 10 minutes. Portion equal amounts of shrimp, scallops and creole sauce in each potato shell. Top each shell with ½ ounce of cheese and place in 425 degree oven for five minutes. Makes 4 servings. 210 calories per serving.

# Shrimp Rockefeller

20 ounces of peeled and
  deveined shrimp
2 cups chopped steamed spinach
½ cup onions, diced

½ teaspoon Pernod
4 ounces MORNAY SAUCE
Vegetable coating spray (Pam)

Place chopped spinach in strainer to drain excess water. Lightly spray a small frying pan with vegetable spray and sauté onions until transparent. Add chopped spinach and Pernod to sautéed onions and mix. Simmer for 5 minutes.

Steam shrimp for 3 minutes. To serve, place ½ cup of spinach mixture on plate, lay 5 ounces of shrimp on top and cover with one ounce of Mornay sauce. Serves 4. 1 serving = 175 calories.

# Scallop Parmesan

16 ounces scallops
4 egg whites
Whole wheat flour for light
  coating
8 ounces MARINARA SAUCE

4 ounces low fat mozzarella
  cheese, grated
2 cups cooked brown rice
Vegetable coating spray (Pam)

## MARINARA SAUCE

¼ cup low sodium chicken broth
1 small onion diced
1 clove garlic, crushed
¾ cup tomato sauce (low
  sodium)

1 teaspoon dry mustard
4 tablespoons lemon juice
½ teaspoon chopped oregano

Combine all marinara sauce ingredients in saucepan; simmer 20 minutes, uncovered. Place a light layer of sauce on bottom of baking pan; set aside.

Combine egg whites and dip scallops into egg white batter, then into whole wheat flour (lightly coat). Place coated scallops into baking pan. Bake in 350 degree oven for seven to ten minutes until scallops are done. Add remaining marinara sauce and grated mozzarella cheese on top. Place back in oven until cheese melts. Serve hot with ½ cup cooked brown rice per serving.

May substitute scallops for:

Shrimp Parmesan
Veal Parmesan
Eggplant Parmesan
Chicken Parmesan

3 jumbo shrimp or 4 large shrimp
2½ ounces veal
4 ounces of uncooked eggplant
3 ounces chicken

175 calories includes 4 ounces of scallops, 2 ounces marinara sauce and 1 ounce mozzarella cheese. Recipe yields 4 servings.

# Shrimp Vin Blanc

12 jumbo shrimp or 16 large
   shrimp
Vegetable coating spray (Pam)

2 cups cooked brown rice
8 ounces VIN BLANC SAUCE

## VIN BLANC SAUCE

1 cup low sodium chicken broth
½ cup dry white wine
½ cup skim milk

2 teaspoons arrowroot (mix with
   water), Mrs. Dash, white
   pepper

On medium heat combine chicken broth, white wine and skim milk; simmer until wine is evaporated. Add arrowroot slowly to sauce until sauce thickens to preference.

Spray skillet with vegetable coating spray, sauté shrimp until done. Add cooked shrimp to Vin Blanc sauce until hot. Serve over brown rice.

May substitute shrimp for:

Scallop Vin Blanc
Seafood Vin Blanc

Fish Vin Blanc

5 ounces scallops
5 ounces seafood (Lobster, crab,
   shrimp)
5 ounces fish (sole, flounder,
   snapper)

175 calories includes 3 jumbo shrimp, 2 ounces Vin Blanc sauce and ½ cup cooked brown rice. Recipe yields 4 servings.

# Oven-Fried Fish Fillets

4 fish fillets, 3 ounces each          ¼ cup evaporated skim milk
4 egg whites, slightly beaten          Cornmeal

Preheat ovenproof platter in 425 degree oven. Dip fish in mixture of egg whites and milk, then dip in cornmeal. Place on hot platter, and bake 25 minutes. Serves 4. 1 serving = 140 calories.

# Crab-Stuffed Sole

1 tablespoon plus 1 teaspoon reduced          ¼ cup minced fresh parsley
   calorie soft (not stick) margarine          ¼ cup sliced scallions
2 teaspoons 100% corn oil          1 large egg white
   margarine          1 teaspoon lemon juice
¼ cup plus 2 tablespoons plain          Dash ground red pepper
   dried bread crumbs          4 3¾ ounces sole fillets
4 ounces thawed cooked Alaskan          ⅛ teaspoon each paprika and
   King crabmeat (from          freshly ground black pepper
   ½ pound leg)

Place margarines in measuring cup; cover and melt in microwave on High (100%) power 15 seconds. Stir in 2 tablespoons of the bread crumbs, the paprika and pepper; set aside. In medium bowl, combine the remaining ¼ cup bread crumbs, the crabmeat, parsley, scallions, egg white, lemon juice and ground red pepper. Spoon ¼ of the crab filling (about ⅓ cup) onto center of each fish fillet. Loosely roll fish around filling; secure with toothpicks. Arrange fish, seam-side down, in 8" square microwave-suitable pan. Spoon reserved crumb mixture evenly over top of each sole roll. Cover pan with vented plastic wrap and microwave on High 5 minutes, giving pan a quarter turn halfway through cooking, until fish is just cooked through and filling is hot. Remove toothpicks before serving. Makes 4 servings. 1 serving = 180 calories.

# Fish Patties

¾ *pound tender-fleshed fish*
  *fillets*
¼ *cup chopped onion*
2 *cups bread crumbs*
1 *cup grated raw potato*

8 *egg whites, beaten to soft*
  *peaks*
¼ *cup evaporated skim milk*
*Pepper*

Chop fish into tiny pieces. Combine all other ingredients, then add fish. Mix well. Drop by tablespoons onto hot Teflon skillet, shape into patties, and fry both sides. Serves 6. 1 serving = 175 calories.

# Fillet of Flounder

1 *pound fillets of flounder or*
  *codfish*
1 *teaspoon paprika*

2 *medium onions, sliced thin*
½ *cup skim milk*

Broil fish on one side until lightly browned. Turn fish over in pan. Sprinkle uncooked side with paprika. Layer on the onions. Pour milk over top, return to broiler and brown. Serves 4. 1 serving = 100 calories.

# Minute Fish

1 *pound fish fillets*
½ *cup dry white wine*
2 *tablespoons chopped green*
  *onion*

2 *tablespoons chopped fresh*
  *parsley*
½ *teaspoon pepper*

Arrange fish in shallow baking dish and pour wine around fish. Sprinkle remaining ingredients over top and bake at 450 degrees until top is browned and fish is cooked (about 15 minutes). Serve from baking dish. Serves 4. 1 serving = 100 calories.

# Baked Fish

*1½ pounds fillet of sole (or other fish)*
*1 cup dry white wine*

*Vegetable coating spray (Pam)*
*Lemon wedges and parsley*

Preheat oven to 350 degrees. Spray ovenproof dish with Pam. Place fillets in ovenproof dish (if fillets are large, cut them in half). Pour dry white wine over fillets. Bake until just done. (Insert thermometer in thickest part of fish. Fish is done at internal temperature of 140 degrees. If you have no thermometer, stick a toothpick into the thickest part of the fish. Fish is done when the flesh is no longer translucent and flakes readily.) Serve with liquid from dish and garnish with lemon wedge and parsley. Serves 6. 1 serving = 110 calories.

# Tuna Loaf

*1 7¾ ounce can of tuna, rinsed and drained*
*3 cups soft bread crumbs*
*½ cup skim milk*
*3 egg whites*

*½ cup chopped onion*
*2 tablespoons parsley flakes*
*½ teaspoon taragon*
*2½ cups CURRIED PEA SAUCE*

Combine all ingredients except pea sauce, mixing and mashing well to distribute tuna, seasonings and wet ingredients thoroughly in bread crumbs. Shape mixture in a 8" × 8" × 2" Teflon pan. Bake 25 minutes at 400 degrees. Pour hot curried pea sauce over entire surface of tuna loaf and serve. Serves 6. 1 serving = 175 calories.

# Broiled Tuna Steaks
# (or Halibut or Salmon)

*3 fresh tuna steaks (approx. 2
    pounds, 1½ inches thick)*
*1 medium lemon*
*Pepper*

*¼ cup dry vermouth*
*¼ teaspoon basil*
*Onion powder*

Rinse steaks under cold running water. Remove excess moisture with paper towels. Sprinkle on both sides with the dry
seasonings. Place steaks in shallow baking pan, no larger than
necessary to accommodate fish. Sprinkle fish with juice of half
of the lemon. Gently pour vermouth over fish. Let marinate 1
to 2 hours, spooning marinade over top occasionally and turning steaks once. Broil 6 inches from heating element. When
lightly browned (10-15 minutes), turn steaks very carefully,
using two pancake turners, one over and one under the steak.
Baste with any excess marinade. Broil 10 to 15 minutes. Serve
immediately and garnish with thin slices of the remaining half
of the lemon. Any juice left in broiler pan makes a delicious
sauce to pour over fish or rice. Serves 6. 1 serving = 175
calories.

# Tuna Noodle Casserole

*3 cups noodles (about 6 ounces)*      *White pepper*
*1 7 ounce can water packed tuna*    *Onion powder*
*1¼ cup low fat cottage cheese*     *Dill weed*
*½ cup skim milk*

Drop noodles into boiling water, stir, cook until done (10 minutes), and drain. Rinse tuna to remove sodium. Combine noodles and tuna. Blend cottage cheese and skim milk and seasonings to taste in blender. Whip until the consistency of a white sauce. Add to noodles and tuna. Mix well (top with bread crumbs if desired). Pour into 1½ quart casserole dish and bake at 350 degrees until top is slightly browned (about 30-35 minutes). Serves 4. 1 serving = 175 calories.

---

| | |
|---|---|
| Shrimp Parmesan | See Scallop Parmesan Recipe |
| Scallop Vin Blanc | See Shrimp Vin Blanc Recipe |
| Seafood Vin Blanc | See Shrimp Vin Blanc Recipe |
| Fish Vin Blanc | See Shrimp Vin Blanc Recipe |
| Seafood Creole | See Chicken Creole Recipe |
| Shrimp Creole | See Chicken Creole Recipe |
| Shrimp Chow Mein | See Chicken Chow Mein Recipe |
| Sweet and Sour Shrimp | See Sweet and Sour Chicken Recipe |
| Blackened Fish | See Blackened Chicken Recipe |

|  | Calories | Protein (g) | Fat* (g) |
|---|---|---|---|
| Bass, striped | 476 | 85.7 | 12.2 |
| Bass, sea black | 422 | 87.1 | 5.4 |
| Bluefish | 530 | 93.0 | 15.0 |
| Bonito | 762 | 108.9 | 33.1 |
| Buffalofish | 513 | 79.4 | 19.1 |
| Butterfish, Gulf | 431 | 73.5 | 13.2 |
| Carp | 522 | 81.6 | 19.1 |
| Catfish | 467 | 79.8 | 14.1 |
| Clams, soft | 372 | 63.5 | 8.6 |
| Clams, hard or round | 363 | 50.3 | 4.1 |
| Cod | 354 | 79.8 | 1.4 |
| Crab | 422 | 78.5 | 8.6 |
| Flounder | 358 | 75.8 | 3.6 |
| Grouper | 395 | 87.5 | 2.3 |
| Haddock | 358 | 83.0 | 0.5 |
| Halibut | 453 | 94.8 | 5.4 |
| Kingfish | 476 | 83.0 | 13.6 |
| Lobster | 413 | 76.7 | 8.6 |
| Mackerel | 866 | 86.2 | 55.3 |
| Mullet, striped | 662 | 88.9 | 31.3 |
| Mussels | 431 | 65.3 | 10.0 |
| Oysters | 299 | 38.1 | 8.2 |
| Perch, ocean | 430 | 86.2 | 6.8 |
| Perch, yellow | 413 | 88.5 | 4.1 |
| Pike, blue | 408 | 86.6 | 4.1 |
| Pike, northern | 399 | 83.0 | 5.0 |
| Pike, walleye | 422 | 87.5 | 5.4 |
| Pollack | 431 | 92.5 | 4.1 |
| Pompano | 753 | 85.3 | 43.1 |
| Porgy | 508 | 86.2 | 15.4 |
| Red Snapper | 422 | 89.8 | 4.1 |
| Rockfish | 440 | 85.7 | 8.2 |
| Salmon, Atlantic | 984 | 102.1 | 60.8 |
| Salmon, Chinook | 1007 | 86.6 | 70.8 |

## SEAFOOD ENTREES

|  | Calories | Protein (g) | Fat* (g) |
|---|---|---|---|
| Sardines, canned in oil, drained | 755 | 89.3 | 41.3 |
| Sauger | 381 | 81.2 | 3.6 |
| Scallops | 367 | 69.4 | 0.9 |
| Shrimp | 412 | 82.1 | 3.6 |
| Smelt | 445 | 84.4 | 9.5 |
| Sole | 358 | 75.8 | 3.6 |
| Sturgeon | 426 | 82.1 | 8.6 |
| Swordfish | 535 | 87.1 | 18.1 |
| Trout, brook | 458 | 87.1 | 9.5 |
| Trout, lake | 762 | 83.0 | 45.4 |
| Trout, rainbow | 885 | 97.5 | 51.7 |
| Tuna, canned in oil, drained | 894 | 130.6 | 37.2 |
| Tuna, canned in water | 576 | 127.0 | 3.6 |
| Whitefish, lake | 703 | 85.7 | 37.2 |

*SOURCE: U.S. Department of Agriculture, Agricultural Research Service. Composition of Foods (Agriculture Handbook No. 8), 1963, 1975. *Figures reflect content of 1 pound of ready-to-cook (or, for canned items, cooked, flesh only.)

## TIMETABLE FOR COOKING FISH

| Method of Cooking | Market Form | Cooking Temperature | Approximate Cooking Time |
|---|---|---|---|
| Baking | Dressed | 350 degrees | 45 to 60 mins. |
| | Pan-dressed | 350 degrees | 25 to 30 mins. |
| | Fillets or steaks | 350 degrees | 20 to 25 mins. |
| Broiling | Pan-dressed | 3 to 4 inches from heat | 10 to 16 mins. Turning once |
| | Fillets or steaks | | 10 to 15 mins. |
| | Frozen fried fish | | 10 to 15 mins. |
| | Frozen fried fish sticks | | 10 to 15 mins. |
| Charcoal Broiling | Pan-dressed | Moderate | 10 to 16 mins. turning once |
| | Fillets or steaks | Moderate | 10 to 16 mins. |
| Oven-Frying | Pan-dressed | 500 degrees | 15 to 20 mins. |
| | Fillets or steaks | 500 degrees | 10 to 12 mins. |
| Pan-Frying | Pan-dressed | Moderate | 8 to 10 mins. turning once |
| | Fillets or steaks | Moderate | 8 to 10 mins. |
| Poaching | Whole Fish | Simmer | 30 to 60 mins. |
| | Fillets or Steaks | Simmer | 5 to 10 mins. |
| Steaming | Filets or Steaks | Boil | 5 to 10 mins. |

*SOURCE: U.S. Department of Agriculture, Agricultural Research Service. Composition of Foods (Agriculture Handbook No. 8), 1963, 1975. *Figures reflect content of 1 pound of ready-to-cook (or, for canned items, cooked, flesh only.)

# POULTRY ENTREES

## Chicken Cacciatore

4 3 ounce chicken breasts,
  skinned
½ cup green onion tops
½ cup green pepper
1 large tomato, diced
½ cup water or CHICKEN
  STOCK

½ teaspoon oregano
½ teaspoon black pepper
2 garlic cloves, crushed
1 bay leaf
8 ounces unsalted tomato juice
2 cups cooked brown rice

Braise chicken breasts with vegetables in a non-stick skillet, adding ½ cup water or chicken stock to prevent sticking. Mix seasonings with tomato juice in a separate bowl. Pour mixture over chicken breasts and vegetables. Cover and simmer for 20 to 25 minutes. Place each serving over ½ cup rice. Serves 4. 175 calories per serving.

# Arroz Con Pollo
### Rice with Chicken

4 3 ounces chicken breasts,
skinned and trimmed of visible
fat
¼ cup dry vermouth
1 cup brown rice
1 cup sliced fresh mushrooms
1 cup chopped onion
2 cloves garlic, sliced

2⅓ cups CHICKEN STOCK
1 28 ounce can of whole
tomatoes
¼ cup chopped pimento
2 tablespoons chopped fresh
parsley
½ teaspoon pepper
Pinch of saffron

Moisten chicken with vermouth, and brown in broiler, three inches from element. With pastry brush, baste frequently to prevent dryness, using cooking juices and water (or chicken broth). Remove chicken when lightly browned and arrange in casserole dish. In separate pan, combine rice, mushrooms, onions and garlic in ¼ cup stock, bring to a boil, cover and simmer 20 minutes at very low heat. Add remaining ingredients, heat to boiling, and pour over chicken in casserole. Cover and bake at 350 degrees for 50 minutes. Remove cover and cook ten minutes more. Serves 4. 1 serving = 225 calories.

# Chicken-Laced Manicotti

¾ pound chicken breast
4 manicotti shells, cooked "al
   dente" and cooled
1½ cups CHICKEN STUFFING

½ cup low fat cottage cheese
3 sprigs of fresh rosemary
2¼ cups MUSHROOM SAUCE

Remove skin, bones and fat from chicken, being careful to preserve the chicken meat in pieces that are as large as possible. Cut chicken into long strips one inch wide. Carefully fill manicotti shells with stuffing, and place stuffed shells in shallow baking dish, leaving ample space between. Wrap chicken strips diagonally around manicotti shells (about two strips per shell). Layer cottage cheese on top of manicotti shells and pour sauce over all. Preheat oven to broil temperature. Insert casserole, and immediately reduce oven setting to 350 degrees. Bake 30 minutes and serve. Serves 4. 1 serving = 200 calories.

# Chicken Breast Paprika

¾ pound of chicken breast
½ cup skim buttermilk
1 teaspoon paprika
1 cup flat or crinkly noodles
2 cups sliced mushrooms
¼ cup chopped onion
½ cup chopped celery

2 tablespoons chopped green
 pepper
½ cup dry vermouth
2 cups MOCK SOUR CREAM
 or low fat cottage cheese
Chopped chives for garnish

Preheat oven to 450 degrees. Remove skin and fat from chicken breasts. Cut the meat from the bones, into fillets. Marinate two hours in buttermilk and paprika. Arrange in a single layer in a flat baking dish, smothered in marinade. (If desired, top with freshly ground pepper.) Bake 20 minutes. While chicken is baking, cook noodles. Meanwhile, sauté vegetables in vermouth, in a covered pan. Boil off excess liquid. Add sour cream (or cottage cheese) and heat gently until warm. Add the cooking juices from the chicken (which by now should be done) and mix. Serve chicken in bed of noodles topped with vegetable-sour cream (cottage cheese) mixture. Garnish with chopped chives. Serves 4. 1 serving = 200 calories.

# Turkey Divan

4 3 ounce skinned, boned
 turkey breasts, sliced
2 cups chopped broccoli

8 ounces CHICKEN SAUCE
Vegetable coating spray (Pam)
2 cups cooked brown rice

Place chopped broccoli evenly over turkey breast slices. Roll slices and insert toothpicks to hold. Place in small baking pan lightly sprayed with Pam and bake in 325 degree oven for 30 minutes. Remove and place on serving plate. Top with two ounces of chicken sauce and garnish with chopped parsley. Serve with ½ cup cooked rice. Serves 4. 175 calories.

# Stuffed Chicken Supreme

*4 3 ounce chicken breasts*  
*8 ounces of FIBER DRESSING*  
  *(STUFFING)*

*8 ounces CHICKEN SAUCE*  
*Vegetable coating spray (Pam)*

Place stuffing evenly on chicken breasts, roll breasts and insert toothpick. Place rolled breasts in a small baking pan lightly sprayed with Pam and bake in a 325 degree oven for 30 minutes. Remove breasts from oven and place on serving plates. Top each with 2 ounces of chicken sauce. Garnish with chopped parsley. Serves 4. 175 calories.

# Chicken Creole

*4 3 ounce chicken breasts*  
  *(skinless)*  
*8 ounces SPA SAUCE*  
*½ cup chopped green pepper*  
*½ medium onion, diced*

*½ cup mushrooms, sliced*  
*2 cups cooked brown rice*  
*Dash of tabasco sauce*  
*Dash of Mrs. Dash*  
*Vegetable coating spray (Pam)*

Sauté chicken on both sides with vegetable coating spray. Remove cooked chicken, put it on a plate and place another plate on top of chicken to keep warm. In the same pan, put in chopped onions, green peppers and mushrooms. Sauté until light brown. Add spa sauce and simmer for two minutes. Add spices and cooked chicken to spa sauce and simmer for five minutes. Serve over brown rice.

May substitute chicken for:

*Shrimp Creole:*

*3 jumbo or 4 large shrimp*

*Seafood Creole:*

*5 ounces seafood (lobster,*  
  *shrimp, crab and scallops)*

175 calories includes 3 ounce chicken breast, 2 ounces spa sauce and ½ cup cooked brown rice. Recipe yields 4 servings. 175 calories per serving.

# Chicken Breast Tarragon

*4 3 ounce chicken breasts*
*8 ounces of CHICKEN SAUCE*
*2 cups cooked brown rice*

*1 tablespoon of fresh ground*
*Tarragon*
*Vegetable coating spray (Pam)*

Take a small baking pan and lightly spray with vegetable oil. Place skinned chicken breasts on baking pan and bake in a 325 degree oven for 30 minutes. While chicken is baking, place the sauce and the fresh tarragon in a small pan and cook over a low flame. Serve chicken with 2 ounces of sauce on top. Serve over brown rice. 175 calories includes a 3 ounce chicken breast, 2 ounces of chicken sauce and ½ cup of cooked brown rice. Makes 4 servings.

# Sherried Chicken Livers

*8 ounces of chicken livers*
*1 cup of cooking sherry*
*2 cups of steamed rice*

*1 cup TOMATO SAUCE*
*1 cup chopped onion*

In a medium size sauté pan, place 4 ounces of cooking sherry and heat until half reduced. Take chopped onion and add to reduced sherry and sauté until onions are transparent. Remove onions from sauté pan and add remainder of cooking sherry to warmed sauté pan. Once the sherry starts reducing, add the chicken livers and let cook until fully browned. Drain off any excess liquid and then add tomato sauce and onions. Simmer until sauce is hot. Place ½ cup of steamed rice on plate and ladle equal amounts of chicken livers over each of the four servings. 205 calories per serving.

# Chicken Chow Mein

4 3 ounce chicken breasts
¼ cup baby corn
¼ cup water chestnuts
¼ cup bamboo shoots
¼ cup straw mushrooms or
  mushrooms
¼ cup leeks or scallions
¼ cup bean sprouts
¼ cup snow peas
2 cups cooked brown rice

¼ cup bok choy (chinese
  cabbage)
2 cups low sodium CHICKEN
  STOCK (mixed with water)
2 tablespoons low sodium
  Tamari Sauce
Fresh ginger, garlic, Mrs. Dash,
  pepper for seasoning to taste
  (no sugar or salt)
Vegetable coating spray (Pam)

Sauté the chicken breasts in the vegetable coated pan, set aside. Sauté the chinese vegetables in the chicken stock until semi-firm, add seasonings to taste. Gradually add the arrowroot to thicken sauce. Place cooked chicken breasts into vegetable sauce until hot. Serve over brown rice.

May substitute chicken for:

Veal Chow Mein                   2½ ounces veal

Shrimp Chow Mein                 3 jumbo shrimp or 4 large shrimp

Beef Chow Mein                   2½ ounces of lean beef

175 calories includes three ounce chicken breast, ½ cup chinese vegetables and ½ cup cooked brown rice. Makes 4 servings.

# Blackened Chicken

*4 3 ounce chicken breasts
  (skinless)
8 ounces SPA SAUCE
2 cups cooked brown rice*

*1 teaspoon low sodium cajun
  seasonings
Vegetable coating spray (Pam)*

Heat pan until very hot. Take pan off of fire, add vegetable coating spray and put back on fire. Pat cajun seasonings on chicken breast, lightly cover the whole breast. Place chicken breast on the fire seasoned side down until blackened. Turn chicken over until it is completely cooked. Serve over brown rice.

May substitute chicken for:

*Blackened fish*                    *5 ounces fish*

175 calories includes 3 ounce chicken breast, 2 ounces spa sauce and ½ cup cooked brown rice. Makes 4 servings.

124

# Sweet and Sour Chicken

4 3 ounce chicken breasts
½ cup chopped onions
½ cup chopped celery
½ cup chopped carrots
½ cup chopped green peppers
1 cup low sodium CHICKEN
  STOCK
¼ cup tomato paste (for color)
  (low sodium)
¼ cup chopped unsweetened
  pineapples
¼ cup chopped unsweetened
  cherries
¼ cup unsweetened pineapple
  juice
1 teaspoon vinegar
1 teaspoon lemon juice
2 tablespoons arrowroot (to
  thicken sauce)
2 cups cooked brown rice
Sugar substitute (to sweeten sauce)
Vegetable coating spray

Sauté the chicken breasts in the vegetable coated pan, set aside. Sauté the vegetables in the chicken stock until semi-firm, add cherries, tomato paste, vinegar, lemon juice, pineapple and juice to vegetables. Gradually add the arrowroot to thicken sauce and sugar substitute for taste. Place cooked chicken breasts into sweet and sour sauce until hot. Serve over brown rice.

May substitute chicken for:

Sweet and sour shrimp                    3 jumbo or 4 large shrimp

175 calories includes 3 ounce chicken breast, ½ cup sweet and sour vegetables and ½ cup cooked brown rice. Makes 4 servings.

# Chicken Stuffed Peppers

*Per serving:*

1 large bell pepper
4 ounces chopped, cooked
  chicken
1 ounce toasted cubed bread
¼ cup chopped celery
1 ounce chopped onion

½ teaspoon sage
¼ teaspoon other seasonings to
  replace salt such as Mrs.
  Dash
½ cup low sodium tomato juice
Pepper to taste

Boil green pepper until tender. Cook chicken, celery, onions, sage, seasoning and pepper together in ½ cup water until tender and almost boiled dry. Mix with bread cubes and stuff pepper. Place in baking dish and mix remaining water and tomato juice (season if desired) to pour over peppers. Bake at 350 degrees for 45 minutes. 175 calories.

# Chicken Française

2 pounds chicken cutlets, very
  thin
2 cups grated Parmesan cheese
3 egg whites slightly beaten

Vegetable coating spray (Pam)
¼ cup diet margarine
1 lemon sliced thin

Rinse chicken; coat with cheese; dip into eggs. Sauté with vegetable coating spray until golden brown on both sides. Melt margarine in 13″ × 9″ × 2½″ baking dish. Dip chicken in margarine on both sides and place side by side in baking dish. Top with lemon slices and bake at 350 degrees for 20 minutes. Serves 8. 1 serving = 225 calories.

# Turkey with Broccoli

¾ pound turkey breast
1 teaspoon vegetable powder
¼ teaspoon pepper
3 cups sprigs of fresh broccoli (2
 to 3 inch sprigs)

3 large mushrooms, sliced thin
¼ cup plus 2 tablespoons dry
 vermouth
1 tablespoon arrowroot
2 cups cooked brown rice

Remove skin and fat from turkey. Cut turkey into one inch cubes and Teflon-brown slightly. In saucepan, combine turkey, vegetable powder, pepper and 1 cup water. Cover and simmer until turkey is done (about 15 minutes). Add broccoli and mushrooms. Stir in a mixture of the vermouth and arrowroot. Continue cooking and stirring until thickened. Serve over brown rice. Serves 4. 1 serving = 225 calories.

# Chicken Noodle Casserole

¾ pound deboned chicken,
 cooked and cut up
8 ounces flat noodles, cooked
 and drained
½ pint low fat, no salt added
 cottage cheese
¼ cup skim milk

¼ teaspoon each:
parsley
oregano
garlic powder
onion powder
thyme
basil
celery seed
cayenne pepper

Blend cottage cheese, skim milk and seasonings in blender until consistency of cream. Combine chicken and noodles, pour on sauce and mix well. Bake at 350 degrees for approximately 20 minutes covered. Serves 4. 1 serving = 175 calories.

# Turkey-Stuffed Cabbage Rolls

1½ cups uncooked brown rice
1 medium head cabbage
2 cups cooked, ground turkey
½ cup chopped onion

¼ cup chopped celery
2 cloves garlic, minced
1 teaspoon basil
1 16 ounce can of tomatoes

Combine rice with 3¾ cups water, bring to a boil, cover and simmer slowly one hour. Boil whole head of cabbage 25 minutes. Peel leaves from cabbage and place on a plate. Mix all ingredients except cabbage leaves and tomatoes. Put a large spoonful of this mixture on each leaf, tuck ends in, roll up, and place them in a casserole. Chop tomatoes and pour tomatoes and juice over all. Bake 50 minutes at 350 degrees. Serves 6. 1 serving = 175 calories.

# Polynesian Chicken

3 pound chicken cut up and
  skinned
3 cloves garlic and 1 small onion
⅔ cup water
¼ cup crushed unsweetened
  pineapple

¼ cup lemon juice
2 tablespoons spicy brown
  mustard
2 teaspoons Sugar Twin
½ teaspoon chili powder
  (optional)

Combine all ingredients except chicken in blender, blend on high speed until everything is liquified. Pour over chicken and marinate 4-5 hours or overnight, turning several times. Preheat broiler. Drain and reserve marinate. Place chicken, skin side down in broiler pan, 8 to 9 inches from heat and broil about 20 minutes on one side, basting with marinade every 5 minutes. Turn and do same on other side. Serves 4. 1 serving = 115 calories.

# Chicken Curry and Rice

3 *pound chicken cut up and*
  *skinned*
2 *small onions chopped*
2 *garlic cloves minced*
2 *tablespoons flour*
2 *teaspoons ginger*

2 *teaspoons cardamom*
2 *tablespoons curry powder*
2 *medium tomatoes chopped*
1 *cup peeled and chopped apple*
2 *cups chicken broth*

Sauté chicken until golden, remove chicken and sauté onion and garlic until tender. Add next 4 ingredients to onion mixture and stir. Add next 3 ingredients, stir and simmer 2 hours. Spoon over rice. Serves 4. 1 serving = 175 calories.

# Chicken Cacciatore and Rice

3 *pound chicken cut up and*
  *skinned*
1 *green pepper cut into 2" pieces*
*Vegetable coating spray*
  *(Pam)*
2 *medium onions chopped*
1 *teaspoon oregano*

1 *pound can tomatoes (low*
  *sodium)*
1 *teaspoon minced garlic*
½ *pound mushrooms sliced*
*Bay leaf*
1 *teaspoon basil*
2 *cups cooked brown rice*

Brown chicken in vegetable coating spray. Remove from pan. Sauté onions, green pepper, mushrooms, garlic, basil and oregano for 5 minutes. Add tomatoes, bring to a boil, reduce heat, cover and simmer for 20 minutes. Add chicken and cook until chicken is tender. Serve chicken and sauce over rice. Can substitute veal or seafood for chicken and can substitute spaghetti for rice. Serves 4. 1 serving = 225 calories.

Chicken Parmesan                    See Scallop Parmesan Recipe

# VEAL · BEEF · LAMB ENTREES

## Marinated Flank Steak

10 ounce flank steak
½ cup low calorie French
  Dressing

Dash of black pepper
Vegetable coating spray (Pam)

Marinate flank steak in dressing and pepper in refrigerator for one hour. Lightly coat frying pan with Pam and cook steak to taste. Serve with ½ cup parsleyed boiled potatoes. Serves 4. 200 calories.

## Veal Florentine

4 2½ ounce portions fresh veal
  cutlets
2 ounces cooked spinach
1 cup chicken broth (low
  sodium)

1 tablespoon arrowroot
1 tablespoon parsley, chopped
Mrs. Dash

De-vein veal and pound with mallot to ½ inch thickness. Braise veal in ½ cup chicken broth and add seasonings. Mix arrowroot with remaining ½ cup broth and add to mixture. Add spinach, simmer 20 to 30 minutes until veal can be broken with a fork. Season to taste. Serve hot with ½ baked potato. Serves 4. 200 calories per serving.

# Veal Parmesan

12 ounces veal loin cutlets
4 ounces part-skim Mozzarella
  cheese

8 ounces TOMATO SAUCE
Vegetable coating spray (Pam)
Sprig of parsley (for garnish)

Slice and tenderize four 3 ounce portions of veal. Slice four 1 ounce slices of Mozzarella cheese. Lightly spray a small frying pan with vegetable cooking oil and sauté veal over a high flame. Place sautéed veal cutlets on a baking pan with 1 ounce of Mozzarella cheese, grated, on top and bake in 350 degree oven for 5 minutes. Remove from oven, cover each cutlet with 2 ounces of tomato sauce and sprig of parsley, and serve. 4 servings. 205 calories per serving.

# Roast Veal

1½ pounds veal
½ head of cabbage (shredded)
¼ teaspoon ground pepper
1 garlic clove (mashed)
2 stalks celery, sliced
1 large onion, sliced
2 carrots, sliced

2 tablespoons tomato paste (low
  sodium)
1 cup dry wine (red preferred)
1½ to 2 cups water
8 to 10 peeled potatoes (red if
  possible)
Juice from 1 large lemon

Rub veal with garlic and pepper. In the bottom of a roasting pan, place the combined onion, celery, carrots and cabbage. Put the veal on top of the vegetables. Then spill the mixed wine, tomato paste, lemon juice and water all over. Place the potatoes around the veal. Cover the roasting pan and set it in a 350 degree oven for a little over an hour. Serves 8. 1 serving = 175 calories.

# Snow Peas and Beef

1 cup cooked, drained lean
   ground beef
2 cups snow peas (about 50
   pods)

1½ cups sliced mushrooms
¼ cup dry vermouth
4 teaspoons arrowroot
3 cups hot, freshly cooked rice

Place beef, peas, mushrooms and vermouth in a Teflon pan. Add arrowroot blended with ½ cup water and cook over medium heat, stirring constantly until thickened. Pour over rice and serve. Serves 4. 1 serving = 225 calories.

# Swiss Steak

¾ pound top round or
   boneless round steak
1½ cups BEEF STOCK
1 8 ounce can of tomatoes
1 cup sliced fresh mushrooms

1 medium onion, sliced
⅛ teaspoon sage
⅛ teaspoon pepper
¼ cup flour
3 cups mashed potatoes

Trim all visible fat from meat. Slowly Teflon brown in a skillet with tight-fitting lid. Pour over meat 1 cup of the beef stock, the tomatoes, mushrooms, onions, sage and pepper. Bring to a boil, cover and simmer 1½ to 2 hours, occasionally checking for adequate liquid and moving and turning meat to prevent sticking. In a small bowl, combine flour with remaining stock. When smooth, stir into Swiss Steak mixture and cook until thickened. Serve over mashed potatoes. Serves 6. 1 serving = 200 calories.

# Hamburger-Corn Skillet Dinner

¾ pound lean ground beef
1 cup soft bread crumbs
½ teaspoon pepper
1 16 ounce can of tomatoes

1 10 ounce package of frozen
   whole-kernel corn
1 small onion, sliced

Mix meat, crumbs and pepper and cook in skillet until meat is
well browned. Drain fat. Add corn, onions and tomatoes, cover
and simmer 25 minutes. Serves 4. 1 serving = 225 calories.

# Easy Stroganoff

3 cups uncooked noodles (or
   other pasta)
½ pound round steak, cut in ½
   inch pieces
½ cup chopped onions

½ cup mushrooms, sliced thin
⅓ cup BEEF STOCK
1 tablespoon arrowroot
½ cup non-fat yogurt

Cook and drain noodles. Brown steak cubes over high heat in
Teflon pan, being careful not to overcook (center of cubes
should remain pink or red). In small covered saucepan, sauté
onions and mushrooms, using ¼ cup water. Remove cover and
boil away most of liquid, stirring constantly. Blend stock with
the arrowroot and combine with the steak cubes and sautéed
onions and mushrooms. Just before serving, heat this mixture
until sauce boils and thickens. Add yogurt and serve over the
hot noodles. Serves 4. 1 serving = 225 calories.

# Lamb Primavera

4 ounces lamb chops with bone
¼ cup sliced onions
1 garlic clove, minced
2 medium tomatoes (blanched, peeled, seeded and chopped)
½ cup water
⅛ cup dry rosé wine
½ cup sliced mushrooms

1 teaspoon tomato paste (low sodium)
¼ teaspoon rosemary
¼ cup peas
½ cup asparagus (steamed)
Vegetable coating spray (Pam)
½ cup cooked brown rice

Broil lamb chops until done (around 2 minutes). Sauté onions, garlic and mushrooms in vegetable coating spray until onions are transparent. Add tomatoes, water, paste, and rosemary to sautéed mushroom mixture. Stir in remaining vegetables and wine. Cook for 3-5 minutes on medium flame. Serve over broiled lamb chops with ½ cup of cooked brown rice. Serves 1. 175 calories.

# Apricot Glazed Lamb Steak

2½ ounces lamb steak
2 tablespoons reduced calorie apricot glaze
½ teaspoon honey
½ tablespoon Tamari Sauce (low sodium)

½ teaspoon mustard (low sodium)
¼ garlic clove, pressed
½ cup cooked brown rice

Mix all ingredients to a glaze mixture. Brush lamb steak with glaze. Broil, turn and glaze the other side. Finish under broiler. Serve with ½ cup of cooked brown rice. Serves 1. 175 calories.

# Tenderloin Kabobs

12 ounces tenderloin, cut into
  1 ounce cubes
1 medium onion cut into eighths
1 bell pepper cut into eighths

8 large mushroom caps
8 small clusters of fresh broccoli
1 cup cooked brown rice

On each skewer, arrange 3 cubes of tenderloin, 2 wedges of each vegetable. Broil 7 to 12 minutes and serve hot over ¼ cup cooked rice. Serves 4. 190 calories.

# Marinated Lamb Brochettes

2½ ounces lamb, cut in 3
  cubes
2 wedges onion

2 wedges bell pepper
2 cherry tomatoes
¼ cup cooked brown rice

## MARINADE

½ cup lemon juice
1 tablespoon water
1 teaspoon honey
1 teaspoon tomato paste (low
  sodium)
1 teaspoon tomato juice (low
  sodium)

½ teaspoon onion powder
½ teaspoon lemon peel
½ teaspoon oregano
¼ teaspoon mint flakes

Mix above ingredients for marinade. Marinate lamb pieces in refrigerator for one hour, turning occasionally. On a skewer arrange alternately 3 cubes of lamb, 2 wedges of onion, green pepper and 2 cherry tomatoes. Broil 7 to 12 minutes and serve hot over ¼ cup of cooked rice. Serves 1. 175 calories.

Veal Chow Mein
Beef Chow Mein

See Chicken Chow Mein Recipe
See Chicken Chow Mein Recipe

# DESSERTS

## Cinnamon Mousse

1 cup prepared whipped
  topping (Dream Whip)
2 egg whites
½ teaspoon cream of tartar

2 teaspoons diet vanilla pudding
  powder
1 teaspoon cinnamon
2 tablespoons water

Place egg whites and cream of tartar in a small mixing bowl. Whip with an electric mixer until stiff peaks form. Add pudding powder, water and cinnamon mixture to prepared whipped topping, mix well, fold in stiff egg whites. Place four ounce servings in dishes and chill before serving. Serves 4. 40 calories.

## Apricot Snow

¾ cup dried apricots
1½ cups boiling water
1 envelope unflavored gelatin
3 egg whites

⅓ cup apple juice concentrate
½ cup orange or pineapple juice
¼ cup cold water

Place apricots in saucepan and cover with boiling water. Allow to stand 1 hour. After apricots have softened, simmer over medium heat 20 to 30 minutes. Cool. Purée this mixture in food processor or blender. Return purée to saucepan. Soften gelatin in cold water and add to fruit purée. Add concentrate and juice to pan and heat mixture 2 to 3 minutes. Beat egg whites until stiff and fold into apricot mixture. Pour into four ounce serving dishes and chill until firm. Makes 6-8 servings. 40 calories.

# Lemon Sponge

2 egg whites
½ teaspoon cream of tartar
½ teaspoon lemon extract

1 cup prepared whipped topping
   (Dream Whip)

Beat egg white with cream of tartar until stiff. Add lemon extract to whipped topping, fold in egg whites, place four ounce servings in dishes and chill at least one hour. Serves 2. 40 calories.

# Applesauce Pudding

1 egg white, beaten until stiff
½ cup prepared whipped topping
   (Dream Whip)

¼ teaspoon cinnamon
¼ teaspoon nutmeg
¼ medium apple, cored

Place apple in blender with nutmeg and cinnamon. Fold this mixture into whipped topping, then fold in the egg whites. Makes 4 four ounce servings. 1 serving = 40 calories.

# Apple Snow

¼ cup fresh puréed red
   delicious apple, with peel
1½ tablespoons apple juice
¼ teaspoon cinnamon

½ cup prepared whipped topping
   (Dream Whip)
1 egg white
¼ teaspoon cream of tartar

Beat egg white with cream of tartar at high speed until stiff peaks form. Set aside. Prepare Dream Whip according to directions, substituting apple juice and puréed apple for part of the liquid called for. Fold beaten egg white into this mixture. Portion into serving glasses and chill at least one hour before serving. Makes 4 four ounce servings. 40 calories.

# Pineapple Coconut Bavarian

2 egg whites
½ teaspoon cream of tartar
1 envelope prepared whipped
   topping (Dream Whip)
1 teaspoon shredded coconut

1 tablespoon Siba pineapple
   coconut delight (Pina
   Colada mix)
6 teaspoons puréed unsweetened
   pineapple, canned or fresh

Beat egg whites with cream of tartar until stiff peaks form. Prepare Dream Whip and add pineapple coconut delight. Fold egg whites into this mixture. Place in dish and chill one hour before serving. Spoon 1 teaspoon pineapple over each portion and garnish with shredded coconut. Serves 6. 40 calories.

# Peach Fluff

1 cup prepared whipped
   topping (Dream Whip)
½ cup boiling water

½ tablespoon diet peach gelatin
   powder
¼ cup puréed peach

Dissolve gelatin and puréed peaches in boiling water. Chill until set. Prepare Dream Whip and set aside. When gelatin mixture is firm, place in mixing bowl and beat until double in volume. Fold in Dream Whip. Portion into 4 ounce servings. Chill at least one hour. Serves 4. 40 calories.

# Strawberry Tart

1 cup prepared whipped
  topping (Dream Whip)
¼ cup puréed strawberries

½ tablespoon strawberry gelatin
  powder
½ cup hot water

Dissolve gelatin and puréed strawberries in boiling water. Chill until set. Prepare Dream Whip and set aside. When gelatin mixture is firm, place in mixing bowl and beat until double in volume. Fold in Dream Whip. Portion into dishes and chill for at least 1 hour before serving. Serves 4. 40 calories.

# Chocolate Mocha Mousse

1 cup prepared whipped
  topping (Dream Whip)
2 egg whites
½ teaspoon cream of tartar
2 tablespoons water

2 teaspoons diet chocolate
  pudding powder
1 teaspoon decaffeinated instant
  coffee

Place egg whites and cream of tartar in small mixing bowl. Whip with an electric mixer until stiff peaks form. Add pudding powder, water and coffee to prepared whipped topping. Mix well, then fold in stiff egg whites. Chill before serving. Serves 4. 40 calories.

# Chocolate Peppermint Mousse

½ package prepared whipped
   topping, ¾ ounce (Dream
   Whip)
1 egg white

1 tablespoon D-Zerta diet
   chocolate pudding
¼ teaspoon peppermint extract

Prepare Dream Whip according to package directions. Add pudding powder and peppermint extract and beat mixture for one minute. Fold in beaten egg whites. Chill well before serving. Garnish with fresh mint leaf. Serves 4. 40 calories.

# Baked Almond Apple

3 red delicious apples, cored
   and halved
2 tablespoons brown sugar
2 cups water

1 teaspoon cinnamon
¼ teaspoon nutmeg
1 teaspoon almond extract

Place half apples flat side down on baking pan. Mix seasoning and extract with water and pour over apples. Bake in 350 degree oven for 40 minutes. Serve warm or chilled. 6 Servings. 40 calories.

# Light Cheesecake

1½ tablespoons plain gelatin
¼ cup hot canned unsweetened
  pineapple juice
¼ cup canned pineapple chunks,
  unsweetened
1½ cups puréed 1% low fat
  cottage cheese

1 packet Sweet 'N Low
¼ cup unsweetened shredded
  coconut
1 cup prepared Dream Whip

Dissolve gelatin in juice. Add coconut and chill until firm but not completely set. Prepare Dream Whip in mixing bowl, add pineapple and Sweet 'n Low and set aside. Combine gelatin mixture with puréed cottage cheese. Beat at medium speed with electric mixer for 2 to 3 minutes. Fold in whipped topping mixture at low speed until blended. Pour into 2 inch deep refrigerator pan. Chill at least 2 hours before serving. Serves 6. 40 calories.

# Fruit Torte

1 8 ounce can low calorie fruit
  cocktail
Lemon flavored low calorie Jell-O

Lady fingers
1 cup prepared whipped topping
  (Dream Whip)

Drain fruit cocktail, measure syrup and add enough water to equal one cup. Bring liquid to a boil and dissolve lemon Jell-O powder in the hot mixture. Stir in one cup of ice and water and continue stirring until the ice melts. Chill until very thick. Line an 8" by 4" pan with split lady fingers. Whip gelatin until double in volume, blend in the Dream Whip and the fruit cocktail. Spoon over lady fingers and chill thoroughly before serving. Serves 8. 40 calories.

# Buttermilk Chiffon Cheesecake

## FILLING

4 cups low fat cottage cheese
1 6 ounce can of frozen apple
  juice concentrate
2 tablespoons unflavored gelatin

1 12 ounce can of unsweetened
  crushed pineapple
3 egg whites, beaten to stiffness

## CRUST

Grape-Nuts

## TOPPING (optional)

1 20 ounce package of frozen
  strawberries

1 tablespoon arrowroot

TO MAKE FILLING: Loosely crumble cottage cheese into blender. Blend until very smooth. Thoroughly dissolve the can of frozen apple juice in 2 cans of water. If contents of blender appear too dry, add a few tablespoons of the apple juice to blender and blend. Combine gelatin and pineapple in large bowl and mix well. Heat 1 cup of the apple juice to boiling, pour over gelatin and pineapple mixture, and stir to dissolve gelatin. Set aside to cool. Beat egg whites to stiffness. Add vanilla and the contents of the blender to the cooled pineapple gelatin mixture, then fold in egg whites.

TO MAKE CRUST: Dampen enough Grape-Nuts with apple juice to cover bottom and sides of two 9-inch pie pans.

TO MAKE TOPPING (optional): Place strawberries in saucepan. Blend arrowroot with 2 tablespoons apple juice, combine with remaining apple juice (there should be about ¾ to ⅞ cup), and add to saucepan. Bring to boil, reduce heat to medium-low, and cook until thickened.

TO ASSEMBLE CHEESECAKES: Pour filling in pie pan, spooning some over middle to make nice rounded form. Spread on topping and refrigerate until firm (about 1 hour). Makes 2 cheesecakes. 1 slice (3″ × 4″) = 125 calories.

# Pineapple Supreme

2 ounces low fat cottage cheese          Lettuce leaf
2 slices unsweetened canned
  pineapple

Place pineapple on lettuce leaf and top with cottage cheese. 60 calories.

# Ice Cream Pie

¾ cup apple juice                    2 cups frozen blueberries
¾ cup non-fat dry milk               2 cups frozen strawberries
2 bananas, sliced                    2½ cups Grape-Nuts

Combine apple juice and dry milk and beat with electric mixer until whipped (works faster if bowl, beater and ingredients are icy cold). Pour half of whipped mixture into blender and blend with fruit, a little at a time, until thick and of an even consistency. Add to remaining half of whipped mixture and mix well. Add 1½ cups of the Grape-Nuts and mix well again. Moisten remaining Grape Nuts and flatten into a layer on the bottom of 2 pie pans. Pour pie mixture into pans and freeze (about 2 hours). Makes 2 pies. 1 small slice (2″ × 4″ × 1″) = 65 calories.

# Orange Sherbet

1 6 ounce can of frozen orange
  juice concentrate
1½ cups skim milk

⅔ cup non-fat dry milk
3 drops vanilla
Grape-Nuts

Combine all ingredients in blender and blend until well mixed. Place in freezer until firm. Serve with topped fresh fruit and Grape-Nuts for crunch. Makes 1½ pints sherbet. ½ cup = 100 calories.

# Fruit Cup

½ cup of fresh fruits

May include orange, grapefruit, pineapple, cantaloupe, honeydew and strawberries. 40 calories.

# Fruit Fluff

Prepared whipped topping
  (Dream Whip)
Puréed fruit (banana, blueberries, strawberries)

1 teaspoon vanilla extract
Dash nutmeg
1 teaspoon lemon juice

Combine all ingredients to prepared Dream Whip topping. Garnish with lemon wheel. 40 calories.

# Apple-Prune Delight

1 prune, finely diced
½ apple, cored and finely diced
½ teaspoon cinnamon
Pinch of nutmeg

2 egg whites
½ teaspoon cream of tartar
1 cup of prepared whipped
   topping (Dream Whip)

In a small mixing bowl combine egg whites and cream of tartar. Beat until stiff peaks form. Set aside. In another mixing bowl, combine the prune, apple, cinnamon and nutmeg with the whipped topping. Mix well. Fold in egg whites. Portion into four serving dishes. Serving size = ½ cup. 60 calories per serving.

# Fruit Pie

2 cups fresh blueberries
2 cups sliced apples
1 cup unsweetened pineapple,
   crushed
1 cup apple juice (unsweetened)
1 teaspoon arrowroot
½ cup rolled oats

¼ cup Grape-Nuts
½ teaspoon cinnamon
1 packet Equal
3 tablespoons apple juice
   (unsweetened)
Vegetable coating spray (Pam)

Combine oats, Grape-Nuts, cinnamon, Equal and 3 tablespoons apple juice. Mix well. Pat mixture into pan (sprayed with Pam) and bake at 350 degrees for approximately 10 minutes. Remove from oven and set aside. Place berries, apples, pineapple and apple juice in saucepan, cover and simmer 15 minutes. Stir in a paste made of arrowroot and 2 tablespoons water. Cook and stir until thickened. Spread thickened fruit mixture over prepared crust. Bake 15 minutes at 400 degrees. Sprinkle additional Grape-Nuts over top and bake 5 minutes more. Makes 1 pie. ⅛ pie = 85 calories.

# Pumpkin Pie

1 1-pound can solid pumpkin
  (unsweetened)
1 8 ounce can crushed
  (unsweetened) pineapple
  (drained)

12 teaspoons flour
9 packages Equal
2½ teaspoons pumpkin pie spice
1⅓ cups dry powdered milk
Vegetable coating spray (Pam)

Combine above ingredients and blend well. Pour into 9 " pie plate sprayed with a vegetable spray (Pam). Bake in preheated 350 degree oven for 1 hour. Makes 1 pie. ⅛ pie = 100 calories.

# Rice Pudding

½ cup uncooked white rice
1½ cups skim milk
2 tablespoons dry non-fat milk
2 egg whites, slightly beaten

2 teaspoons raisins
½ teaspoon vanilla
6 packages Equal
Cinnamon, nutmeg

Bring rice and 1 cup water to a boil. Cover and simmer 15 minutes. Combine all other ingredients except cinnamon and nutmeg and add to rice mixture. Pour into casserole dish and sprinkle with cinnamon and nutmeg and bake 1 hour at 300 degrees. Serves 4. 1 serving = 90 calories.

# Gelatin Parfait

1 package Shimmer Gelatin
  raspberry or strawberry/banana
Piece of fresh fruit (for garnish)

1½ cups CREAMY COTTAGE
  CHEESE

Prepare gelatin from package instructions and cottage cheese mixture. When gelatin is set, place ¼ cup in bottom of parfait glass, spoon ¼ cup cottage cheese mixture on top, alternate gelatin then cottage cheese mixture again. Optional: garnish with one piece of fresh fruit, such as a strawberry. Makes 4 parfaits. 1 parfait = 60 calories.

# Ice Cream
## (Fruit Flavored)

2 medium bananas
1 cup frozen strawberries or
  blueberries or peaches
  (unsweetened)

¼ teaspoon vanilla
2 packages Equal
¼ cup skim milk

Peel bananas, wrap in foil and freeze for several hours. Chop bananas into small slices (approximately 1" long). Place banana in blender with ⅛ cup skim milk and blend at medium speed turning blender on and off to combine bananas and milk (consistency should be lumpy). Add strawberries (or other fruit) a few at a time, add Equal, vanilla and enough milk to make a creamy consistency. Do not over blend. It is done when it is mixed and mixture has the look of ice cream. (Will not freeze.) Serves 4. One serving size = ½ cup. 60 calories.

# Frozen Fruit

1½ cups fresh frozen
  blueberries
1½ cups fresh frozen green,
  seedless grapes

1 cup CREAMY COTTAGE
  CHEESE dressing for fruit

Combine frozen grapes and blueberries and place in serving dishes. Top with sweetened creamy cottage cheese mixture and serve immediately. Makes 4 one cup servings. 1 serving = 90 calories.

# Cream Sickles

8 ounces plain non-fat yogurt
4 tablespoons orange juice
  concentrate

2 packages Equal
½ teaspoon vanilla

Combine all ingredients. Mix well and freeze individually or in a large bowl. Serves 4. 1 serving = 60 calories.

# Apple Crisp

3 apples, cored and diced with
   skin
½ cup unsweetened apple
   concentrate
1 tablespoon arrowroot
3 cups water
3 packets (1½ teaspoons) Sugar
   Twin

1 tablespoon cinnamon
1 dash ginger
½ teaspoon nutmeg
1 teaspoon vanilla extract
CRUST MIXTURE

Mix arrowroot with 1 cup cold water. Add remaining ingredients and bring to a boil in large saucepan. Simmer 20 minutes. Pour mixture into rectangular baking dish (9 × 12) (non-stick surface preferable). Spoon crust mixture over this and bake 20-25 minutes at 350 degrees or until crust is brown. Cut into 12 squares. 1 square = 40 calories.

## CRUST MIXTURE

½ cup whole wheat flour
2 teaspoons baking powder
½ teaspoon Sugar Twin
⅓ cup unsweetened granola or
   raw oats

2 teaspoons safflower oil
1 egg white
½ cup water

Mix dry ingredients together. In separate bowl, mix oil and egg well. Fold mixture together and add water. Let stand 5 minutes. Mix only until ingredients are blended. Avoid over mixing. Gently spoon mixture over apple mixture. 1 serving = 35 calories.

# Chocolate Pudding

1 envelope D-Zerta chocolate
  pudding
1 envelope unflavored gelatin
1 tablespoon instant decaf.
  coffee powder

2½ cups skim milk
½ cup Coffee Rich
1 envelope D-Zerta whipped
  topping

Mix first five ingredients in saucepan and cook over low heat,
stirring until it comes to a boil. Cool. Whip 1 envelope D-Zerta
whipped topping and fold into cooled pudding with a whisk.
Serves 6. 1 serving = 100 calories.

# Sugarless Health Cookies

2½ tablespoons diet margarine
10 pitted dates, chopped fine
18 walnut halves, chopped fine
3 tablespoons raisins
½ teaspoon vanilla

¼ teaspoon baking soda
1¼ cup whole wheat flour
  stirred
½ teaspoon Sweet N' Low
2 egg whites

Cream margarine until soft. Place raisins in hot water to soften.
Mix and sift dry ingredients. Place nuts and fruits in this
mixture. Beat egg whites until fluffy, add Sweet N' Low.
Mix margarine and egg whites, then add flour mixture in
thirds, stirring gently. Drop by teaspoon on greased cookie
sheets. Preheat oven to 375 degrees. Bake 12-15 minutes until
brown. Remove immediately from pan. Makes 1 dozen cookies.
1 cookie = 80 calories.

# Sugarless Oatmeal Cookies

½ cup uncooked oatmeal
⅔ cup melted diet margarine
4 egg whites, slightly beaten
3 teaspoons Sugar Twin
1½ cups sifted whole wheat
   flour
2 teaspoons baking powder
Grated rind of one orange

½ cup skim milk
1 teaspoon vanilla
½ cup raisins
1 tablespoon cinnamon
½ cup chopped walnuts
1 tablespoon instant decaf. coffee
   powder

Mix oatmeal and margarine. Blend in egg whites and Sugar Twin. Add dry ingredients alternately with milk and vanilla. Add other ingredients, mix well. Drop by teaspoonful on greased cookie sheets. 375 degrees. 10–15 minutes. 4–5 dozen (can be frozen). 1 cookie = 30 calories.

# Quick Cappucino Mousse

¼ cup cold water
1 tablespoon plain gelatin
1¼ cups hot espresso coffee

½ teaspoon cinnamon
1 pint low fat vanilla or sugar
   free ice cream

Put cold water in blender then sprinkle on gelatin. Wait one minute until gelatin is soft then add hot coffee and cinnamon. Cover and blend until gelatin is dissolved. Add ice cream a little at a time. Cover and blend after each addition. Spoon into 6 dessert cups. Chill until set. Serves 6. 1 serving = 30 calories.

# Angel Food Cake

*1 cup sifted cake flour*
*¼ cup Sugar Twin*
*1 cup egg whites (8 to 10 eggs)*

*¾ teaspoon vanilla extract*
*¼ teaspoon almond extract*
*1 teaspoon cream of tartar*

Sift ¼ cup sugar twin and flour together four times. Beat egg whites and cream of tartar until foamy. Add remaining sugar a little at a time, beating in well. Add flavorings and beat until very stiff. Fold flour into egg white and sugar mixture, sifting small amount at a time. Pour into 10″ ungreased tube pan. Cut through with spatula to remove air bubbles. Bake in a slow oven (275 degrees) 30 minutes. Raise heat to 300 degrees and bake until done. Invert pan over bottle neck for one hour before removing from pan. ¹⁄₁₂ cake = 45 calories.

# SPICES & BEVERAGES

## Apple Milk

*Equal portions of apple juice and skim milk*

*Mix apple juice and skim milk. Serve immediately, topped with nutmeg and cinnamon if desired. ½ cup = 40 calories.*

## Banana Shake

*1 very ripe banana*  
*1 cup skim milk*

*1 tablespoon non-fat dry milk*  
*3 ice cubes*

Chop and mix in blender until ice dissolves. ½ cup = 90 calories.

## Apricot Cooler

*4 canned apricot halves, water*  
*or juice packed*  
*Fresh mint (for garnish)*

*2 ice cubes*  
*½ cup skim milk*

Place all ingredients in blender, blender-chop to break up ice cubes, then blender-mix for about 30 seconds. Pour into glass, removing undissolved ice. Garnish with fresh mint, if desired. Makes 1 glass. 80 calories.

# Zippy Tom

1 quart salt-free tomato or V-8
 juice
4 lemons
1 teaspoon chili powder

Pepper
Garlic powder
French's Herb Seasoning
4 celery stalk tips, with leaves

Combine tomato juice, the juice of the lemons, and the chili powder. Season to taste with pepper, garlic powder and herb seasoning. Serve with stalk of celery in each glass. Makes 4 eight ounce servings. 1 serving = 50 calories.

# No-Salt Herb Blend

4 tablespoons oregano leaves
4 tablespoons onion powder
4 teaspoons marjoram leaves
4 teaspoons basil leaves
4 teaspoons ground savory

4 teaspoons garlic powder
2 teaspoons thyme leaves
2 teaspoons rosemary leaves
1 teaspoon sage leaves
1 teaspoon ground black pepper

In a bowl combine ingredients. Crush a small amount at a time with a mortar and pestle or with the back of a spoon, or put in a blender and blend together. Spoon into a shaker or tightly covered container. Use over fish, chicken, salads, vegetables, etc.

# Salt-Free Herb Seasoning

2 teaspoons dried dillweed or
   basil leaves, crumbled
2 tablespoons onion powder
1 teaspoon dried oregano leaves,
   crumbled

1 teaspoon celery seed
¼ teaspoon grated, dried lemon
   peel
Pinch of freshly ground pepper

Combine all ingredients.

tabouli ~

- 1/4 cup cracked wheat
- 3/4 cup hot water
- 2 cups chopped parsley
- 1/4 cup chopped fresh mint
- 1/2 cucumber, peeled & diced
- 1 tomato, diced
- 2 scallions, sliced thin
- 3 tablespoons lemon juice
- 3 tablespoons oil
- 1/4 teaspoon salt
- olives (optional)

Soak wheat in $H_2O$ for about 15 minutes to soften. Drain well, squeezing out all moisture. Toss parsley, mint, cucumber, tomato, scallions + soaked wheat together in a serving dish. Coat with lemon juice, oil + salt + mix well. Garnish w/ olives if desired. Chill salad.

# ALL ABOUT SPICES

| SPICE | DESCRIPTION | USES |
|---|---|---|
| Allspice | Resembles a blend of cinnamon, cloves and nutmeg. | Whole: Meats<br>Ground: Baked goods, relishes, fruits |
| Anise | Licorice-flavored fruit of small plant grown in Spain and China. | Baked goods. |
| Basil (Sweet Basil) | Leaves and stems of plant from the mint family. | Tomato dishes, peas, squash, string beans, and soups. |
| Bay leaves | Aromatic leaves of laurel tree. | Stews, sauces, soups, fish, chowder and meats. |
| Cardamom | Dried fruit of plant of the ginger family. | Baked goods. |
| Caraway Seeds | Dried fruit of plant of the parsley family. | Baked goods, cabbage and noodles. |
| Cayenne Pepper | Spicy small peppers, very pungent. | Meats, sauces and fish. |
| Celery Seeds, Powder | Seed of member of parsley family, not the same as celery used as a vegetable. | Salads, salad dressings and vegetables. |
| Chervil | Leaves of an herb grown in many countries in the temperate zone. | Soups, salads, French dressing, fish and chicken. |
| Chili Powder | Blend of chili peppers and other spices. | Mexican dishes, shellfish, sauces and stews. |
| Coriander (Cilantro) | Dried ripe fruit of herb of the parsley family. | Whole: Baked goods and mixed green vegetables.<br>Ground: Rolls. |

159

| SPICE | DESCRIPTION | USES | |
|---|---|---|---|
| Cinnamon | Bark of tree grown in Eastern countries. | Whole: | Stewed fruits and hot drinks. |
| | | Ground: | Baked goods and mashed sweet potatoes. |
| Cloves | Bud of clove tree grown in Eastern countries. | Whole: | Stews and fruits. |
| | | Ground: | Baked goods and vegetables. |
| Cumin | Small dried fruit of parsley family. | Soups, cheeses and pies. | |
| Curry Powder | Blend of many spices. Important in dishes of India. | Vegetables, French dressing, fish, meat and fish chowder. | |
| Dill | Small, dark seed of dill plant from India. | Salad, soups, fish, sauces and spiced vinegar. | |
| Fennel | Small seedlike fruit with sweet taste somewhat like anise. | Fish. | |
| Garlic | Commonly used plant for fresh flavoring. Strong flavor. Used ground form and as cloves. | Salads, salad dressings, meats, soups, sauces, especially tomato, fish, poultry, and vegetables. | |
| Ginger | Root of tuberous plant grown in Asia and Africa. | Whole: | Applesauce. |
| | | Ground: | Baked goods, fruits and meats. |
| Mace | Fleshy, orange-red material between nutmeg shell and outer husk. | Whole: | Fish. |
| | | Ground: | Baked goods and noodles. |
| Marjoram | Herb of mint family. | Stews, soups, fish and poultry. | |
| Mint | Dried leaves, strong sweet flavor. | Soups, stews, beverages, meats, fish and sauces. | |
| Mrs. Dash | Blend of 14 herbs and spices, predominant flavors are lemon and garlic. | Soups, stews, sauces, vegetables, meat, poultry, fish, salads and salad dressing. | |
| Mustard | Small seed grown in U.S. and Europe. Classified as a spice. | Whole: | Salad, fish and meat. |
| | | Dry: | Meats and sauces. |

| SPICE | DESCRIPTION | USES |
|---|---|---|
| Nutmeg | Kernel of nutmeg fruit. | Ground: Baked goods, sauces, fruits and cauliflower. |
| Onion | Commonly used plant for fresh flavoring. | Salads, salad dressings, meats, soups, sauces, especially tomato, fish, poultry and vegetables. |
| Oregano | Dried leaves of herb of mint family. Similar in flavor to marjoram, but stronger. | Pork, beef stew and tomato sauces. |
| Paprika | Colorful red garnish for many foods. | Chicken, fish, salad dressing, meats and vegetables. |
| Parsley | Dried leaves of parsley used in cooking as well as a garnish. | Soups, salads, meat, fish, sauces and vegetable dishes. |
| Pepper | Small dried berry of a vine native to the East Indies. A very important and popular spice. | Whole: Soups and meats. Ground (Black and white): Meats, sauces, vegetables, soups and salads. |
| Rosemary | Dried leaves of evergreen shrub of the mint family. Sweet and fresh tasting. | Lamb, soups, stews, beef, fish and stocks. |
| Saffron | Dried part of the flower of the crocus family. The world's most expensive spice. | Baked goods, rice and chicken. |
| Sage | Dried leaves of herb of the mint family. A very popular herb. | Pork, fish, poultry and green salad. |
| Savory | Dried leaves of herb of the mint family. | Meats, chicken, fish and sauces. |
| Tarragon | Dried leaves and flowering tops of herbs, tastes similar to anise. | Sauces, salads, chicken, meats, tomato dishes and vinegar. |
| Thyme | Dried leaves of plant of mint family. | Stew, soups, poultry, fish chowder, sauces and tomatoes. |

| SPICE | DESCRIPTION | USES |
|-------|-------------|------|
| Tumeric | Root of plant of ginger family. Ingredient of curry powder. | Meats, salads, usually in combination with mustard, fish and seafood. |

*Any other blend of salt-free seasoning can be used, such as Vegit.*

# INDEX